Editor
Julia Lee

Art Editor
Sheradon Dublin

Consultant Editor
Mark Rasmussen

Advertisement Manager
Jay Jones

Advertisement Executive
Alan Dean

Advertisement Production
Sam Valentine

Publisher
Joanna Pieters

An IPC Media annual published by IPC Country & Leisure Media from: Focus Network, Leon House, 233 High Street, Croydon CR9 1HZ.
Tel: 020 8726 8000
Fax: 020 8726 8299

Distributed by
MarketForce, King's Reach Tower, Stamford Street, London SE9 1LS.
Tel: 020 7633 3300

Pre-press by CTT; printed by Stones, Unit 10, Acre Estate, Wildmere Road, Banbury, Oxfordshire OX16 3ES.

BRI COINS

MARKET VALUES 2007

CONTENTS

SPECIAL FEATURES

LATEST MARKET PRICES

This gold Double Leopard of Edward III sold for £460,000, doubling the previous record for a British coin

3

Auctioneers and Valuers

of all types of

Coins, Tokens, Commemorative Medals, Orders, Decorations, Medals and Militaria, Banknotes and Numismatic Books

Eight comprehensive auctions annually.
For further details, please contact Christopher Webb.

DIX NOONAN WEBB

16 Bolton Street   Piccadilly   London W1J 8BQ   England
Telephone   020 7016 1700   Fax   020 7016 1799
E-mail   coins@dnw.co.uk

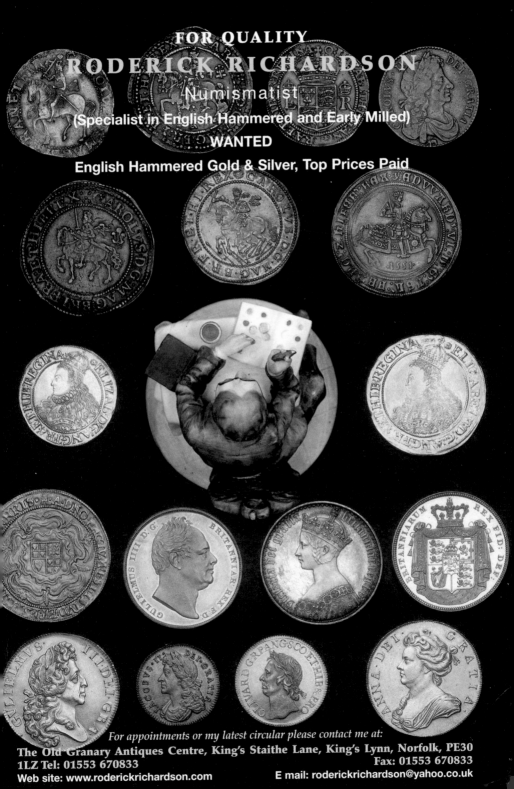

The year in coins

Read on to find out the biggest sellers at the coin auctions held over the last 12 months and the state of the British coin market

The 2005-06 season has been a very successful one for the British coin market. Rising prices have encouraged sellers and there has been a ready supply of interesting material in most sections of the market.

Important sales of copper, bronze, Scottish and Irish coins have supplemented the general sales, and strong demand has continued to push price levels upwards.

The results include a new record for a British coin, £460,000 for the gold Double Leopard of Edward III.

A sensational new record for a British coin was achieved at £460,000 for the gold Double Leopard of Edward III

Autumn auctions

In autumn 2005, Baldwin's began by offering the William C Boyd collection, including 500 lots of British coins.

A beautiful 1839 Victoria pattern silver crown with the Una and the Lion reverse by W Wyon sold for £28,750.

Dix Noonan Webb's sale included both varieties of the very rare 1649 Commonwealth crown which realised £6,250 and £11,500 respectively.

At Spink's Coinex auction a lovely First Coinage portrait penny of Alfred the Great, estimate £1,200-£1,500, sold for £2,645.

The highlight of St James's auction number 3 was a completely unrecorded Standing Knight type penny of William of Aumale, Earl of York.

It was purchased for £9,775 by the Fitzwilliam Museum, Cambridge.

Hoard sells

The Bazas hoard, found in 2004, was sold by auction in France.

It contained English nobles, ryals and angels from Henry V to Richard III, as well as Anglo-Gallic gold and silver coins.

British dealers were active participants and a Richard III angel, in almost very fine condition, fetched £5,750.

The late autumn season was crowned by Spink's double bill, the Ivan Buck collection and the Colin Adams collection of halfcrowns.

Buck's collection of English medieval silver coins attracted almost frenzied bidding from a packed saleroom. In the afternoon session, an unusually fine 1643 Oxford triple unite sold for £64,400.

The Colin Adams collection is the most complete specialist collection of halfcrowns ever assembled. Interest was focused on high grade type coins, and a 1644 Charles I Exeter declaration halfcrown, which had been purchased by Adams in 1996 for £2,860, now realised £16,100.

A 1839 Victoria pattern silver crown with the Una and the Lion reverse sold for £28,750

New year

Heritage's January auction in New York achieved £28,000 for an Edward VIII 1937 proof brass threepence.

But the trade is not all one way: an unusually fine Richard III silver groat, sold by Heritage for

£1,850, was repatriated to the 'old country'.

February saw the sale by Spink of Lucien LaRiviere's Irish coins and medals.

This was the first comprehensive type collection of Irish coins since 2000, and it included many of the great rarities of the series.

The famous Ormonde gold pistole commanded £77,625, a new price record for an Irish coin.

On March 28, Bonhams offered the first portion of the Clarendon collection, which ran from Celtic to Edward VI and was noticeable for the extensive runs of gold coins including a Henry VI Calais rosette-mascle noble, the last noble ever struck at the Calais mint. Purchased in 1990 for £2,200, it now realised £5,400.

A fine example of the very rare Henry VIII First Coinage sovereign, bearing the type of his father's last issue, for £14,100.

Scottish sale

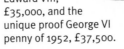

A previously unrecorded Standing Knight type penny of William of Aumale, Earl of York went to a museum for £9,775

Spink's auction number 179 offered Lucien LaRiviere's companion collection of Scottish coins and medals.

They included a magnificent 1575 James VI gold £20 piece and an exceptional 1582 James VI silver 40s piece. They realised £55,200 and £26,450 respectively.

Many collectors appreciate the personal touch that a dealer can supply and the opportunity to examine items outside the pressured atmosphere of the auction room.

Mark Rasmussen's Spring 2006 list contained a wide array of quality material.

The cover coin, the magnificent large bust sovereign of Henry VIII from the Bergne, Montagu and Lockett collections, was unpriced in the list.

It sold for £26,400 in the Strauss sale in 1994 and is probably now a six-figure coin.

The famous Ormonde gold pistole commanded £77,625, a new price record for an Irish coin

The 1933 penny, at £45,000, was complimented by both the proof 1937 penny of Edward VIII, £35,000, and the unique proof George VI penny of 1952, £37,500.

A First Coinage portrait penny of Alfred the Great sold for £2,645

Summer season

The 2006 summer had three important offerings of the elusive copper and bronze series.

On May 2, Baldwin's sold the first portion of the Gregory Collection of British bronze and copper coins in 366 lots.

A week later Colin Cooke sold the impressive collection of farthings assembled over more than forty years by the late Colin D Cooke.

In June, DNW offered the late Laurie Bamford's collection of Victorian bronze pennies to feverish bidding.

Spink's auction number 182 held a surprise, a newly discovered example of the spectacular Double Leopard of Edward III.

Found by in the south of England, only two other examples of this superb piece are known, both now in the British Museum.

There were three bidders still in contention at £370,000 and the realised price of £460,000 is comfortably a new record for any British coin.

Celtic Coins

There have been several good offerings of Celtic coins at auction during the last year, usually as the first element in more general collections of British coins.

The price of Celtic coins is still being restrained by the possibility of new discoveries.

The highest price realised during the year was for a well struck example of the Ambiani A stater, sold for £3,000 during DNW's auction number 70.

This year, gold staters have risen slightly, while the silver and copper examples, particularly in lower grades, have stabilised or declined slightly.

English Hammered Gold

English hammered gold continues to be the powerhouse of the British coin market.

The flagship English hammered gold denominations, nobles, sovereigns and unites have tripled in value in the last ten years but still remain affordable by real terms.

The last noble ever struck at the Calais mint, this Henry VI Calais rosette-mascle noble, managed to realise £5,400

Hammered gold is often inexpensive and can be bought for under £1,000.

Very rare varieties, particularly of the smaller denominations, may be available for less than £2,000. The Clarendon collection contained an attractive gold halfcrown of Henry VIII bearing the initials HI, signifying Henry and his wife Jane Seymour. Far from common, it sold for £1,034.

As hammered gold coins are pure and decorative they are easily damaged, which will significantly reduce the value.

English Hammered Silver

The hammered silver series starts in the Dark Ages with the gemlike little silver sceats produced by the ecclesiastical and secular authorities of the early Anglo-Saxon period and runs right through to the introduction of machine-made coinage in the reign of Charles II.

The supply of new Saxon material has fallen in recent years and the coins are now, once again, rising in value. Demand for good quality examples of the more common types outstrips supply and the sale of material from old collections is keenly anticipated.

The medieval silver market, from Edward III to Richard III, has been a strong one for many years, and the sale of the Buck collection showed a deep

A gold halfcrown of Henry VIII bearing the initials HI, signifying Henry and his wife Jane Seymour, sold for £1,034.

reservoir of demand for this series in all grades of rarity and condition.

A light coinage groat of Henry IV, almost fine and cracked, which cost £275 in 1992 now realised £1,265, while a cleaned but almost very fine example sold for £5,635.

Tudor and Stuart portrait coins are popular, particularly shillings, though condition is now of paramount importance.

A magnificent Charles I Tower mint pattern shilling, mintmark rose, which had sold for £9,750 in 2003, was re-offered by St James's in October 2005. Purchased by a dealer for £13,250, it later found a buyer at £19,950.

Milled Gold

In 2005 the Samuel King and Cheshire collections offered a surfeit of high grade milled gold coins.

The last year has seen relatively few, though several major pieces have been sold privately.

Mark Rasmussen's Spring 2006 list included the superb Charles II proof 1670 five guinea piece which sold for £23,000 when last offered in 1992.

It is possible that good milled gold coins now lag behind the hammered gold in price.

Five guinea pieces graded extremely fine, which were fetching up to £1,000 forty years ago and £5,000

A Charles I Tower mint pattern shilling, mintmark rose, sold at auction for £13,250

thirty years ago, still catalogue for less than £10,000.

Of the ten top prices paid at auction for milled gold coins during the last year, five, all between £22,000 and £28,000 each, were for examples of the 1839 Victoria Una and the Lion £5 piece. The Una £5 is a fabulous coin but it is not a true rarity. During the 1990s the Una and the Lion £5 was overpriced, in the saleroom and in price lists.

Only now, when the market value has caught up with the book price is the Una at last beginning to appreciate in value.

Milled Silver

The sale of the Colin Adams collection dominated this year's market.

The milled section of this collection consisted of a comprehensive run of halfcrowns, from Cromwell to Elizabeth II, sold in 529 lots, from the rarest type coins, proof and pattern issues, right down to minute edge and lettering error varieties.

The 76 halfcrowns of Charles II included perhaps the finest known example of the 1666 halfcrown without elephant below, sold for £3,910.

The excessively rare 1667 halfcrown, graded fair to fine, went for £2,875 and the Charles II 1673 halfcrown with plume below bust and in the centre of the reverse, fetched £16,100 against an estimate of £4,000-5,000.

The Adams collection was particularly strong on the finely-made pattern and proof issues of the 19th century.

An extraordinary run of eleven 1884 Victoria Jubilee head patterns by Edgar Boehn, of which only one example had previously been known, sold for between

A Charles II 1673 halfcrown with plumes below the bust and in the centre of the reverse achieved £16,100

A Cromwell farthing, possibly the finest in private hands of the unusual variety BMC 391, realised £7,800

£3,680 and £5,520.

Milled silver crowns are a strong market in the higher grades.

The John Kenney collection, sold by Spink in March 2006, had several examples including an unusually fine specimen of the common William III first bust crown of 1696. This specimen sold in 1950 for £6 10s, and in 1993 for £451. It now realised £2,750.

At the other end of the scale, Bonhams' July 2006 general sale included a collection devoted to Cromwell and the Commonwealth.

The Cromwell coins included two

crowns, six halfcrowns and no fewer than ten shillings. The halfcrowns, all duplicates, sold for between £425 in fair condition and £2,900 in extremely fine. The shillings, all worn, went for between £185, fair and plugged, and £825 in good fine condition.

Copper and Bronze

The highlight of an exceptional year for copper and bronze coins was the sale of the Cooke collection of British farthings, the most comprehensive run of this most interesting series ever assembled.

A Cromwell farthing, possibly the finest in private hands of the unusual variety BMC 391, realised £7,800.

A superb James II tin issue of 1686 sold for £3,750 and two examples of the excessively rare Victoria 1877 bronze proof farthing for £5,250 and £5,400

Victorian bronze is a particularly strong market and the Bamford collection of bronze pennies took advantage of this interest.

The pennies of 1863 with the die number below the date are much sought after. The Bamford die number 2, perhaps the finest known, sold for £4,600. Die number 3, which was only fine, went for £2,760, and an example of the excessively rare die number 4, catalogued only as mediocre, for £2,300.

Baldwin's sale of the first part of the Gregory collection of British bronze and copper coins added to a memorable season.

A Victoria proof 1860 copper halfpenny sold for £6,900, and one of only four known examples of the George V 1933 pattern penny by Andre Lavrillier for £18,975.

The last example of this piece to be offered, in 2003, had realised £9,775.

Scottish Coins

It has been said that a definitive type collection of Scottish gold requires the acquisition of fifty coins. The Lucien LaRiviere collection, Spink's auction number 179, contained fifty-six gold coins, with a superb range of silver, making it the finest Scottish type

A James VI gold lion noble of 1584 sold for £17,250

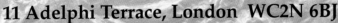

collection to be offered for many years.

The market has recently been subdued and lovely Scottish pieces can be purchased for relatively modest sums.

The LaRiviere results were strong. A magnificent James VI gold lion noble of 1584 which was purchased at the Strauss sale in 1994 for £5,500 now sold for £17,250.

A gold unit by Nicholas Briot, the rare variety with B before the legend, sold for £4,140.

Collector interest drove the price of a James VI Third Coinage silver 1581 4s piece, creased and fair but reputedly the only example of the denomination in private hands, to £2,990, well above the estimate of £600-800.

Irish Coins

The Lucien LaRiviere Irish coins formed a type collection which would do credit to any museum.

The Ormonde gold pistole, struck in 1646, is the pinnacle of the Irish series, and the

A Victoria 1859 proof mule penny, struck from a British penny obverse and a 1839 Manx coinage reverse cost £3,220

LaRiviere piece, at £77,625, is the only one of the three examples in private hands to possess a historic provenance. The early Hiberno-Norse pennies, struck in Dublin in the 10th and 11th century are of great interest for many copies of English types.

A very rare phase V penny, derived from the Pax type of Harold II, sold for £2,300, and a similarly rare piece imitating the Canopy type of William the Conqueror made £2,415.

LaRiviere possessed one of only two known Irish coins of Edward III, a Dublin halfpenny struck in 1339-40 which fetched £7,475.

The Irish irregular coinage struck during the Great Rebellion is, like the English

A superb little gold angelot of Henry VI achieved £7,800

A rare Cork shilling, dated 1647, went for £7,130

Civil War issues, perennially popular.

A rare Cork shilling, dated 1647, sold for £7,130. The corresponding, but much more common, 1647 Cork sixpence sold for £4,140.

The Charles II St Patrick's coinage of copper halfpennies and farthings has recently escalated in price because of an American connection.

In 1681 at least 10,000 halfpennies, issued by the Duke of Ormonde as Lord Lieutenant of Ireland in 1667-69, were taken to America and made current in the Province of West Jersey. A proof St Patrick's farthing struck in silver, in good fine condition, realised £8,625.

Spink's auction number 182 in June 2006, offered the extremely comprehensive Hilary F Guard collection of coins of the Isle of Man.

Many of the coins are very rare, including a Victoria 1859 proof mule penny, struck from a British penny obverse and a reverse of the 1839 Manx coinage at £3,220. The corresponding 1860 proof mule halfpenny reached £3,335 and the farthing went for £2,645.

Anglo-Gallic Coins

Anglo-Gallic coins, when available, are selling well and the problem is one of supply.

The Bazas Hoard contained a useful selection of Anglo-Gallic gold coins, including an almost extremely fine fourth issue Leopard of Edward III, £5,000, and a very rare Pavillon d'Or of Edward the Black Prince without a mint letter, very fine, £3,600.

The Saluts d'Or of Henry VI were struck at Paris, Amiens and Rouen, with one piece from the very rare mint of Chalons, in good to very fine condition fetched £2,900.

In January 2006 Classical Numismatic Group's auction 71, achieved £7,800 for a superb little gold angelot of Henry VI, struck at the St Lo mint. In June the same firm's auction 72 offered an interesting group of Anglo-Gallic deniers and oboles of Richard I, which has provided the series with a number of significant hitherto unrecorded varieties.

How coins are made

The long history of the Royal Mint from its medieval beginnings in the Tower of London to the high-tech processes used today at Llantrisant

ABOVE: Coin blanks pour out of an annealing, or softening, furnace

The production of coins in the United Kingdom goes back to the first century BC, although in those days it was often a case of using very basic moulds for casting.

The coins of Iron Age Britain ceased to be used after the arrival of the Romans. They introduced their own coins, some of which were minted in London.

Later coins were individually struck using hand-held tools, a process which remained unaltered for around 1,500 years, until to the reign of Charles II.

Mints were scattered throughout the country, albeit mainly in the market towns in southern England.

It's thought there were about 30 in Alfred the Great's time (871-899), growing to more than 70 by the reign of Ethelred II (978-1016), although after the Norman Conquest the number started to drop.

The moneyers would operate in what were basically blacksmiths' shops, hammering out blanks between a pair of dies.

During the second half of the 12th century those working in London began to operate from a single location.

At first this was at Old Change, close to the goldsmiths' area in Cheapside.

However, by 1279 it had moved to the Tower of London, where the Royal Mint would remain for the next 500 years.

It occupied a horseshoe shape on three sides of the Tower between the inner and outer walls.

The buildings were certainly secure, but as

mechanisation came in during the 17th century, the accommodation proved very cramped.

The advent of steam-driven machinery at the end of the 18th century led to the decision to move the Mint.

The place chosen was nearby at Tower Hill, previously the site of tobacco warehouses. Before the Reformation it had been home to the Cistercian Abbey of St Mary of Graces.

Work started on the new complex in 1805 and the transfer was virtually complete by 1811.

It was designed by James Johnson and completed by Robert Smirke.

The buildings housing the 'stupendous and beautiful' machinery were separated from the main building by an open quadrangle.

The compound included homes for the staff, and the boundary wall was patrolled by the Mint's own military guard.

The years would see a constant process of renewal and expansion, as the need for coins grew and the processes became more sophisticated.

By the middle of the 20th century it was recognised that the Mint would need to be rebuilt, not least because in 1971 Great Britain would switch to decimal currency, necessitating a vast minting programme.

In 1967, the announcement was made that the new Mint would be built at Llantrisant, ten miles west of Cardiff.

Building started immediately, and the first phase was opened by the Queen on December 17, 1968.

For a while, the premises at Tower Hill were retained, and it was only once the initial bulk requirement for decimal coinage had been met that operations in London were eased off.

In 1975 the melting, rolling and blanking facilities were moved to Llantrisant.

The final coin, a gold sovereign, was struck at Tower Hill in November 1975.

The buildings were finally relinquished in 1980, although for some years the Mint retained an office in central London.

The site at Llantrisant occupies around 38 acres, and uses the latest technology to produce of coins and medals.

It remains a department of government with the main responsibility of producing the United Kingdom coinage, although it has also provided coins for over 100 countries worldwide.

Design

Most British coin designs are arrived at by competition. Freelance artists and the Royal

ABOVE: An 18th century picture of the Mint after its move to Tower Hill

LEFT: *The Royal Mint Advisory Committee at work, including its former President, Prince Philip (second left)*

BELOW: *Metal for coins is melted in an electric furnace*

BOTTOM: *Coils of metal waiting to go into the blanking presses*

Mint's own engravers are invited to submit ideas.

Sometimes the competition is open, such as when the new £2 coin was introduced.

The submitted designs are viewed by an independent panel known as the Royal Mint Advisory Committee.

Its choice is initially put to the Chancellor of the Exchequer, who is Master of the Mint. He then seeks the approval of the Queen.

Since the reign of Charles II, British coins have shown a portrait of the monarch on the obverse. The direction in which the monarch faces traditionally changes with each reign. The portrait of Queen Elizabeth II faces to the right. In fact, four different portraits have been used during her reign.

From 1952 to 1999, the President of the Advisory Committee was His Royal Highness Prince Philip, with the Deputy Master of the Mint as Chairman.

Since 1999, a Chairman has been appointed for a fixed term, with the Chief Executive of the Mint becoming the *ex-officio* Deputy Chairman.

In 1999, the Committee reviewed its thinking to improve the quality of designs submitted.

It began to examine general portfolios as a better way of selecting artists and to offer higher payment for the preliminary stages to encourage more time for research and the generation of ideas.

The current appointed Chairman, the first, is Professor Sir Christopher Frayling, Rector of the Royal College of Art and Chairman of the Arts Council England.

Members of the Committee normally serve for

Coin Case "Aluminium"

for over 190 Coins

- Aluminium coin case
- Comfortable handle and lockable catch
- Dark blue velour
- Complete with 6 trays with space for 190 coins
- Size: 250 x 215 x 70 mm

Item-No: 176   **£13.50** (plus £4 p and p)

ABOVE: The strip left after the coin blanks have been punched out at a rate of 10,000 a minute

a period of seven years.

Whatever the Committee may decide, the final arbiter is the public, and not all designs meet with universal approval, such as the 2005 design for the sovereign.

The production process

The chosen design is produced in the form of a cast, normally by the Mint's own engravers working from the artist's drawing.

In the Engraving Department, the designers use traditional modelling and hand-engraving as well as the latest computer design software.

At one time the casts would have been reduced to coin size to produce the dies using a pantograph.

Today, however, the design is scanned and processed and computers help cut the steel for the master tools.

The initial stages in the minting of coins are melting, rolling and blanking.

Raw materials, such as copper, nickel, zinc and recycled metal scrap are melted in an electric furnace.

The metal is drawn out of the furnaces in continuous strips and then cut into coils of up to 2.8 tonnes.

These are reduced to the required thickness in tandem rolling mills, before being transferred to the blanking presses where the coin blanks are punched out at a rate of 10,000 a minute. The left-over strip is returned to the furnaces for re-melting.

The blanks then pass through a rimming machine that raises the edge of the blanks to protect the design of the coin from wear.

The blanks are softened in an annealing furnace and then cleaned in the pickling plant, where they are washed to remove staining and polished ready for striking.

They then pass to the coining presses where the obverse and reverse are stamped out between a pair of engraved dies. Milled edges are simultaneously added onto the blanks. Each Rhodes coin press can stamp out 850 coins a minute.

By the late 1990s much of the equipment at Llantrisant, in use since the plant opened, was reaching the end of its useful life. At the same time, the UK 1p and 2p coins began to be made out of cheaper copper-plated steel. Two new plating plants were therefore installed, bringing

ABOVE: An annealing furnace softens the blanks

COINS MARKET VALUES

ROYAL MINT

A TRADITION OF EXCELLENCE

The Royal Mint can trace a continuous history spanning more than eleven centuries.

Minting began in Britain as early as the first century BC, but the earliest notable milestone in the history of the Royal Mint can be traced back to Alfred the Great when in 886 he occupied London, already a 'most renowned place and royal town' and celebrated his victory with a spectacular issue of silver pennies.

By 1279 the moneyers had come together within the safety of the Tower of London where greater emphasis was give to the weight and fineness of the King's coinage. However, it wasn't until the reign of Henry VII that coins, through their designs, became powerful symbols of national pride and a medium to confer honour and glory to the English throne.

Although the Royal Mint relocated to Tower Hill in 1812 and to a purpose built site in Llantrisant in 1968, there remains an unbroken link from the scattered workshops of Anglo-Saxon moneyers to the world-class facilities in South Wales today.

This marriage of time-honoured skills and state-of-the-art technology is epitomised in the Proof coins struck by the Royal Mint each year for discerning numismatists around the world.

From the silver pennies of Alfred the Great to the gold nobles of medieval kings, from the illustrious gold sovereign to the new bi-coloured £2 coin, the Royal Mint can rightly claim to span three millennia, at the same time tracing the social, economic and political history of the nation.

To see the full range of Royal Mint products visit our secure website at:
www.royalmint.com

or contact our Customer Services Team on:
0845 60 88 300
or write to us quoting ref : CYB07 to:
Royal Mint, FREEPOST NAT23496, PO Box 500, Pontyclun CF72 8BR

LEFT & BELOW: A modern Trial of the Pyx at the Hall of the Worshipful Company of Goldsmiths, and a 19th century one at the Office of the Comptroller-General of the Exchequer, Whitehall

the Mint's capacity to 30,000 tonnes a year.

A high-energy burnishing machine was also installed to improve the quality of blanks, as was equipment that implants security devices in coins.

After striking, the coins pass through an automatic counting machine, ready to be bagged and boxed for onward transmission. The contents are then checked by weight.

A high level of accuracy is essential, so the composition of the alloy is constantly checked using x-ray fluorescence spectrometry.

Standards are also maintained by the rigorous annual quality examination undertaken by the Worshipful Company of Goldsmiths, known as the Trial of the Pyx.

This ceremony has been taking place since 1282, and involves an independent jury that checks the weight, diameter and composition of the United Kingdom's coins.

The Queen's Remembrancer presides over the

proceedings, with the Freemen of the Goldsmiths' Company and officers of the National Weights and Measures Laboratory also in attendance.

A selection of coins is weighed to check the average weight, the composition is tested against known standards, and the diameters are measured. In each case, the test is to ensure the coins fall within the prescribed tolerances.

What are the coins in your pocket made of?

£2	outer ring	nickel brass	76% copper, 4% nickel, 20% zinc
	inner section	cupro-nickel	75% copper, 25% nickel
£1		nickel-brass	70% copper, 5.5% nickel, 24.5% zinc
50p		cupro-nickel	75% copper, 25% nickel
20p		cupro-nickel	84% copper, 16% nickel
10p		cupro-nickel	75% copper, 25% nickel
5p		cupro-nickel	75% copper, 25% nickel
2p		*	97% copper, 2.5% zinc, 0.5% tin
* bronze until September 1992, copper-plated steel thereafter			
(except in 1998 made in both copper-plated steel and bronze)			
1p		*	97% copper, 2.5% zinc, 0.5% tin
* bronze until September 1992, copper-plated steel thereafter			

COINS MARKET VALUES

Tips for collecting

If you are new to the numismatic hobby or have just stumbled across an old family collection in the loft, here is some vital advice to get you started and put you in touch with the experts

How much is it worth?

There was a time when newcomers to coin collecting would ask the question 'What is it?'

Nowadays, the most common question dealers hear is 'What is it worth?'

The aim of *British Coins Market Values* is to try to place a value on all the coins produced in what is known geographically as the British Isles, in other words England, Wales, Scotland and Ireland, and the Channel Islands, as well as the Anglo-Gallic series.

This is a difficult task because many coins do not turn up in auctions or lists every year, even though they are not really rare.

However, we can estimate a figure so that you, the collector, can at least have an idea of what you will have to pay.

How to sell at auction

In England we are well served with a number of auction houses, giving the potential seller considerable choice.

In London alone there are several: Baldwin's, Bonhams, Dix Noonan Webb, Morton and Eden in association with Sotheby's, and Spink.

There are also smaller companies up and down the country, such as Croydon Coin Auctions.

The best approach for the seller is to compare the auction house's catalogues and if possible attend the auctions so that you can see how well they are conducted.

Talk over your collection with the auction house's experts, for you may have special cataloguing requirements and you may find that one of the firms will look after them better than the others.

A well-known coin, for example an 1887 £5, requires little expertise and will probably sell at a certain price in almost any auction.

However, if you require cataloguing of a specialism like countermarked coins or early medieval, then you need to know what a company is capable of before you discuss a job rate.

You should remember that, while it is not complicated to sell by auction, you may have to wait three or four months from the time you consign the coins to the auctioneers before you receive any money.

There are times when items at auction manage to achieve very high prices, and other times when, for some inexplicable reason, they fail to reach even a modest reserve.

You should also bear in mind that the best deal

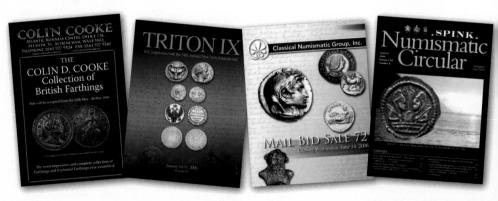

in the long term is not always the one with the lowest commission rate.

Finally, auctioneers will usually charge you at least 10% of the knock-down price, and will charge the buyer a premium of around 15%.

Dealers

The function of a dealer is to have a stock of coins for sale at marked prices. However, they will only wish to buy according to the ebb and flow of their stocks.

It is also true to say that dealers infinitely prefer fresh material, and if you strike at the right time you could achieve a better price than by waiting for an auction, and of course you will receive the money immediately.

Generally speaking, both dealers and auctioneers will not make any charge for a verbal valuation, but you should allow for the dealer to be making a profit of at least 20%.

Bullion coins

Bullion coins can be priced by looking at the price of gold, which is fixed twice daily by a group of leading banks. Most newspapers carry this in their financial pages.

Anyone can buy bullion coins, such as sovereigns or Krugerrands, and in most cases they are not subject to VAT.

Normally, when you sell a bullion coin you expect the coin dealer to make a few pounds profit on each coin.

Do not, however, expect a good price for a mounted coin attached to a watch chain, which will not be worth anything like an undamaged item.

Also, read up and learn more about the market.

How to collect coins

You should obviously purchase your coins from a reputable dealer.

You can be sure of some protection if you choose a member of the British Numismatic Trade Association or the International Association of Professional Numismatists.

Membership lists can be obtained from the respective secretaries:

■ Mrs Rosemary Cooke, PO Box 2, Rye, East Sussex TN31 7WE.
Tel/Fax: 01797 229988. E-mail: bnta@lineone.net
■ Jean-Luc Van Der Schueren, 14 Rue de la Bourse, B 1000 Brussels, Belgium.
Tel: 0032 2 513 3400. Fax: 0032 2 513 2528.

However, many dealers are not members of either organisation, and it does not mean that they are not honest and professional.

The best approach is simply to find one who will unconditionally guarantee that the coins you buy from him are genuine and accurately graded.

As a general rule, you should only buy coins in the best condition available. At first you will have to rely on the judgement of your chosen dealer.

However, remember it will not always be possible to find pieces in Extremely Fine condition and it can sometimes be worth buying coins which are not quite Very Fine.

In the case of great rarities, of course, you might have to make do with a coin that is only Fine, or even Poor.

If there are only six known specimens of a particular piece, and four are in museums, it is pointless to wait 20 years for another one to be found in the ground.

Over the last few years, condition has become too important and driven away collectors.

Only buying coins in top condition would rule out at least 50 per cent of the available specimens in certain series. It very much depends on the type of coin, the reign it comes from and other factors, so be realistic.

It is worth taking out subscriptions with auction houses so that you receive their catalogues, because this is an excellent way to keep up with prices as well as the collections that are being offered.

However, one should not overlook the fact that a number of dealers produce price lists, so you can chose coins at leisure by mail order.

It is also easier to work out what you can afford to buy than when in the hot-house atmosphere of the auction room.

The most famous list is Spink's *Numismatic Circular*, first published in 1892 and still going strong with 10 issues a year.

It is more than a price list, being an important forum for numismatic debate, the reporting of new finds and other useful information (annual subscription £20 in the UK).

There are also many expert dealers who produce excellent lists. A good cross section of those who list domestic coins, in alphabetical order, follows:
■ A H Baldwin & Sons, 11 Adelphi Terrace, London WC2N 6BJ. Hammered and milled.
■ Lloyd Bennett, PO Box 2, Monmouth, Gwent NP5 3YE. Hammered, milled, tokens.
■ B J Dawson, 52 St Helens Road, Bolton, Lancashire BL3 3NH. Hammered, milled, tokens.
■ Dorset Coin Company, 193 Ashley Road, Parkstone, Poole, Dorset BH14 9DL. All coins and banknotes.
■ Format, 18-19 Bennetts Hill, Birmingham B2 5QJ. All British.
■ Grantham Coins, PO Box 60, Grantham, Lincolnshire. Milled, good on Maundy.
■ K B Coins, 50 Lingfield Road, Martin's Wood, Stevenage, Hertfordshire SG1 5SL. Hammered and milled.
■ Knightsbridge Coins, 43 Duke Street, St James, London SW1Y 6DD. Hammered and milled.
■ Peter Morris, PO Box 223, Bromley, Kent BR1 4EQ. Hammered, milled, tokens.
■ Spink & Son, 69 Southampton Row, Bloomsbury, London WC1B 4ET. Hammered and milled.

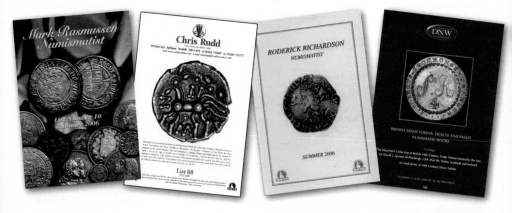

- S R Porter, 18 Trinity Road, Headington Quarry, Oxford OX3 8QL. Hammered and milled.
- Mark Rasmussen, PO Box 42, Betchworth, Surrey RH3 7YR. Hammered and milled.
- Roderick Richardson, The Old Granary Antiques Centre, King's Staithe Lane, King's Lynn, Norfolk PE30 1LZ. Hammered and milled.
- Chris Rudd, PO Box 222, Aylsham, Norfolk NR11 6TY. Celtic coins.
- Classical Numismatics Group (Seaby Coins), 14 Old Bond Street, London W1X 4JL. Hammered, some milled.
- Simmons & Simmons, PO Box 104, Leytonstone, London E11 1ND.

Societies

Consider joining your local numismatic society, of which there are over 50 across the UK. To find if there is one near you, get in touch with the British Association of Numismatic Societies: Mr P H Mernick, c/o General Services, 42 Campbell Road, London E8 4DT. Tel: 020 8980 5672. E-mail: bans@mernicks.com. www.coinclubs.freeserve.co.uk

The BANS organises annual congresses and seminars, and it is a good idea for the serious collector to consider attending these. Details are published in the numismatic press.

Collectors who wish to go further can apply for membership of the British Numismatic Society. As a member, you receive a copy of the *British Numismatic Journal*, which has details of current research, important articles and book reviews.

The Secretary of the BNS is Lieutenant-Commander C R S Farthing RN, 10 Greenbanks Gardens, Wallington, Fareham, Hampshire PO16 8SF. Tel: 01329 284661.

Coin Fairs

Whilst it is important to visit museums to see coins, it is worth remembering that there is often a fine array on show at coin fairs around the country, and most dealers do not mind showing coins to would-be collectors, even if they cannot afford to buy them on the spot.

The UK's premier international numismatic show, the BNTA Coinex show, will be held at the prestigious venue of Earls Court, London on September 29 and 30.

For more information call the BNTA Secretary, Rosemary Cooke on 01797 229 988. E-mail: bnta@linone.net

Howard and Frances Simmons of Simmons Gallery organise the London Coin Fairs at the Holiday Inn, Bloomsbury, London (formerly the Post House, Bloomsbury). They take place in February, June and November. For all enquiries contact Frances Simmons on 0208 989 8097 or visit www.simmonsgallery.co.uk

The Croydon team of Davidson and Monk organise regular shows at the Jury's Hotel, Russell Street, London. To find out about dates and times ring 0208 656 4583 or visit www.lindamonkfairs.co.uk

Michael Veissid organises the monthly Midland Coin and Stamp Fair on the second Sunday of every month at the National Motorcycle Museum in Birmingham. For further details, call 01743 246 963 or visit www.midlandcoinfair.co.uk

There are also biannual coin and stamp fairs held at York racecourse in January and July by Trevor Davis and Chris Rainey. To find out more ring 01793 513 431, 0208 946 4489 or 01425 656 459 or visit www.stampshows.co.uk

Coin housekeeping

Here are some helpful hints, along with some of the best accessories on the market, to help you keep your collection in good condition

ABOVE: Wooden coin cabinets are produced by Peter Nichols in St Leonards-on-Sea

Storage

Store coins carefully, as a collection which is carelessly or inadequately housed can suffer irreparable damage.

Water vapour causes corrosion and therefore coins should not be stored in damp attics or spare bedrooms but, where possible, in evenly heated warm rooms.

One must be careful only to pick up coins by the edges, as sweaty fingerprints contain corrosive salt.

Wooden cabinets

A collection carefully laid out in a wood cabinet looks very impressive.

Unfortunately, custom-built wooden cabinets are not cheap.

Their main advantages are the choice of tray and hole sizes, and because the manufacturer is often himself a collector, he only uses well-matured woods.

One of the best makers of wood cabinets is Peter Nichols of St Leonards-on-Sea, East Sussex. Tel: 01424 436682.

If you cannot afford a new cabinet, then a secondhand one may be the answer.

These can sometimes be purchased at coin auctions or from dealers but it can be hard to find one with tray hole sizes to suit your coins.

Do-it-yourself cabinet makers should be careful not to use new wood, which will contain corrosive moisture. Use wood from an old piece of furniture.

Albums, plastic cases and carrying cases

There are many of these on the market, some both handsome and inexpensive.

There are also attractive Italian and German-made carrying cases for collectors. These can be obtained from a number of dealers, but Collectors' Gallery, 22 The Parade, St Mary's Place, Shrewsbury, Shropshire SY1 1DL are the UK distributors. Tel: 01743 272140.

Coin albums, where the coins are contained in cards with crystal clear film windows, claim to prevent oxidisation. The cards slide into pages in the album, which is a convenient method of storage, especially for new collectors.

Lindner Publications, Unit 3A, Hayle Industrial Park, Hayle, Cornwall TR27 5JR, supplies useful coin and collecting boxes, as well as albums. Tel: 01736 751910. Fax: 01736 751911.You can also visit the company's website at www.stampaccessories.net

An extended range of Lighthouse coin accessories, including presentation and carrying cases, are available from the Duncannon Partnership, 4 Beaufort Road, Reigate, Surrey RH2 9DJ. Tel: 01737 244222.

Crystalair Compression packs immobilise items between two layers of clear, inert, polyurethane film that moulds to the object placed between it. They are perfect for storing and transporting valuable and delicate items that also need to be viewed.

For details contact Lane Packaging, Headley Park 8, Headley Road East, Woodley, Reading,

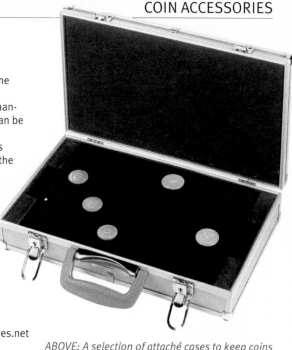

ABOVE: A selection of attaché cases to keep coins in are available from the Duncannon Partnership

Berkshire RG5 4SA. Tel: 0118 944 2425. www.lanepackaging.com

In Central London, the best place to visit is Vera Trinder, 38 Bedford Street, London WC2 E9EU which keeps a good stock. Tel: 020 7836 2365.

Envelopes

Transparent plastic envelopes are very useful for exhibitions, but not recommended for long-term storage purposes.

They tend to make the coins 'sweat' which, can lead to corrosion.

Manila envelopes are much more suitable since the paper is dry. Most collectors use them with a cardboard box, a simple, unobtrusive and inexpensive method of coin storage.

The best article on coin and medal storage is by L R Green, who is Higher Conservation Officer at the Department of Coins and Medals at the British Museum. It appeared in the May 1991 issue of Spink's *Numismatic Circular*.

Cleaning coins

Every week, coin dealers examine coins which someone has unwittingly ruined by cleaning.

BELOW: Leuchtturm cleaning baths for brass, copper, silver and gold are available from the Duncannon Partnership in Reigate

Never clean coins unless they are very dirty or corroded. 'Dirt' does not mean oxide which, on silver coins, can give a pleasing bluish tone favoured by collectors.

Do not clean extremely corroded coins found in the ground, because if they are important, they will be handed over to a museum conservationist.

Gold coins

Gold should cause collectors few problems, since it is subject to corrosion only in extreme conditions such as a long spell in the sea.

A bath in methylated spirits will usually improve a dirty gold coin. But gold coins should not be rubbed in any way.

*ABOVE:
Lindner coin
boxes are available
in standard clear format
or smoked glass format. 130
variations are available*

Silver coins

Silver coins will discolour easily, and are susceptible to damp or chemicals in the atmosphere. Gentle brushing with a soft, non-nylon, bristle brush will clear loose dirt.

If the dirt is deep and greasy, a dip in ammonia and careful drying on cotton wool should work.

There is no need to clean a coin that has a darkish tone.

Copper and bronze coins

There is no safe method of cleaning copper or bronze coins without harming them. Use only a non-nylon, pure bristle brush to deal with dirt. There is no way of curing verdigris (green spots) or bronze disease (blackish spots) permanently so do not buy pieces with these problems, unless they are very inexpensive.

Remember looking after your coins could make you money in the future!

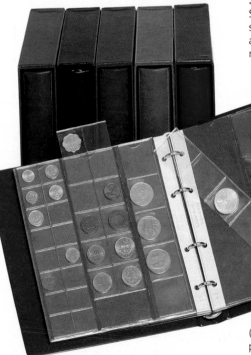

*ABOVE: Lindner Karat coin album supplied with
10 assorted pages, optional slipcase available*

Museum collections
Here's a round-up of the best places to see coins on display in the UK

London, The British Museum
The Department of Coins and Medals boasts the country's premier numismatic collection, most of which is on permanent display.

Collectors can enjoy access to the museum's coin cabinets by special appointment.

Recent acquisitions include the Rogers collection of English silver halfpennies and farthings comprising some 1,360 pieces.

The museum also owns the unique Anglo-Saxon gold penny or *mancus* of Coenwulf.

The Keeper of Coins is Joe Cribb, British Museum, Great Russell Street, London WC1B 3DG. Tel: 0207 323 8607.

Edinburgh, National Museums of Scotland
The Museum of Scotland has the most important collection of Scottish coins in the country.

Highlights include one of the two known specimens of the excessively rare Henry and Mary Ryal of 1565, acquired in 2002.

Visitors are welcome by appointment. The Senior Curator of Numismatics is Nick Holmes, Royal Museum, Chambers Street, Edinburgh EH1 1JF. Tel: 0131 247 4061.

Glasgow, Hunterian Museum
The Hunterian Museum has a permanent numismatic gallery covering Roman,

ABOVE: *The Hoxne hoard, buried in the 5th century*

Copyright: The British Museum

Anglo-Saxon and medieval British coins.

The museum has around 1500 Roman gold coins, as well as one of the four known David II nobles and the unique portrait penny of Eadwig.

The entire museum will be undergoing refurbishment but will re-open in March 2007.

The Senior Curator of Coins and Medals is Professor Donal Bateson, Hunterian Museum, University of Glasgow, Glasgow G12 8QQ. Tel: 0141 330 4289.

Cardiff, National Museum and Gallery
The integral theme of the comprehensive collection is the numismatic history of Wales.

The museum possesses two important hoards, the Bridgend hoard of Roman coins and the Tregwynt hoard of Civil War coins.

The Assistant Keeper in charge of coins is Edward Besly, Department of Archaeology and Numismatics, National Museum and Gallery, Cathays Park, Cardiff CF10 3NP. Tel: 0292 057 3291.

Birmingham, Museum and Art Gallery
Birmingham Museum has one of the largest regional collections in England, with important Celtic, Saxon, Norman and medieval coins.

Some items can be viewed on-line but visits are by appointment only.

The Curator of Antiquities and Numismatics is Dr David Symons, Birmingham Museum and Art Gallery, Chamberlain Square, Birmingham B3 3DH. Tel: 0121 303 4622.

Cambridge, The Fitzwilliam Museum
The Department of Coins and Medals enjoys a rich numismatic collection, much of which is on permanent display.

A major strength is the museum's Saxon and Norman collections.

Certain items from the collection can be accessed via the Department's website. Visitors are welcome by appointment.

The Keeper of Coins and Medals is Dr Mark Blackburn, Fitzwilliam Museum, Trumpington Street, Cambridge CB2 1RB. Tel: 01223 332917.

Oxford, The Ashmolean Museum

The museum's Heberden Coin Room contains a comprehensive collection of Roman, Celtic and medieval coins.

Highlights include a magnificent 1645 'Oxford Crown' of Charles I and an impressive selection of Anglo-Saxon gold Thrymsas.

It is currently closed until the end of 2008.

The Keeper of the Heberden Coin Room is Chris Howgego, Ashmolean Musuem, Beaumont Street, Oxford OX1 2PH. Tel: 01865 278 058.

York, Yorkshire Museum

The museum is strong on Roman coinage, Northumbrian stycas, English hammered silver coins and trade tokens.

Hoards such as the 4th Century Heslington Hoard and single finds from Yorkshire are well represented, as well as Roman, Viking and medieval artefacts.

The Curator of Access-Archaeology is Andrew Morrison, Yorkshire Museum, Museum Gardens, York YO1 7FR. Tel: 01904 687 620.

Belfast, Ulster Museum

The museum houses the best collection of banknotes in Ireland.

The museum will be closed from until late 2008, so the coin collections will be in temporary storage. However, access may be granted.

For all enquiries please contact the Ulster Museum, Botanic Gardens, Belfast BT9 5AB. Tel: 02890 383000.

Dublin, National Museum of Ireland

This museum has the most important collection of Irish numismatic items.

The collection includes the former collection of the Royal Irish Academy.

LEFT: The unique Anglo-Saxon gold penny of Coenwulf
Copyright: The British Museum

It also contains significant hoards such as seven of the 11 known specimens of the exceedingly rare Ormonde gold pistoles.

The Curator of Coins is Michael Kenny, Keeper of the Art & Industrial Division, National Museum of Ireland, Collins Barracks, Benburb Street, Dublin 7, Eire. Tel: +353 1677 7444.

Other important UK museums

Other museums with collections of British coins:
- Blackburn Museum & Art Gallery, Museum Street, Blackburn, Lancashire BB1 7AJ. Tel: 01254 667130
- City Museum, Queen's Road, Bristol BS8 1RL. Tel: 01179 223571.
- Royal Albert Memorial Museum, Queen Street, Exeter, Devon EX4 3RX. Tel: 01392 665858.
- Manx Museum, Douglas, Isle of Man IM1 3LY. Tel: 01624 648000.
- The Leeds Museum Resource Centre, Moorfield Road, Yeadon, Leeds, West Yorkshire LS19 7BN. Tel: 01132 146526.
- Manchester Museum, The University of Manchester, Oxford Road, Manchester M13 9PL Tel: 0161 275 2634.
- Reading Museum, Blagrave Street, Reading, Berkshire RG1 1QH Tel: 0118 939 9800.

Information on holdings

A useful guide entitled *Museums and Select Institutions in the UK and Ireland with Holdings of Numismatic Material* has been put together by Peter Preston-Morley, priced at £5.

Many museums have co-operated with the British Academy to produce a series of books called the *Sylloge of Coins of the British Isles*, now running to more than 50 volumes.

Most are listed on the British Academy's website: www.britac.ac.uk/pubs/cat/scbi.html

Reading material

If your numismatic library is looking a bit empty have a look at our directory of suggested titles to expand your knowledge of coins

We have included the prices you can expect to pay, but as some of the books are long out of print they can only be obtained secondhand, indicated in the list by SH

■ Allen, M, *The Durham Mint*, British Numismatic Society Special Publication number 4, 2003. 222pp, 12 plates. £45. The first book to be published on the Durham Mint since 1780

■ Bateson, J D, *Coinage in Scotland*, 1997. 175pp, well illustrated. £20. The most up-to-date narrative account of Scottish coins in print

■ Bateson, J D, *Scottish Coins*, Shire Publications number 189, 1987. 32pp, illustrated. £2. A useful little introduction to the subject. The Shire Publications are always good value

■ Besly, E, *Coins and Medals of the English Civil War*, 1990. 121pp, beautifully illustrated. SH

■ Besly, E, *Loose Change, a Guide to Common Coins and Medals*, 1997. 57pp, £6.95

■ Blunt, C E, Stewart, B H I H, Lyon, C S S, *Coinage in 10th Century England*, 1989. 372pp, 27 plates. £60

■ Buck, I, *Medieval English Groats*, 2000. 66pp, illustrated. £15

■ Byatt, D, *Promises to Pay: The First Three Hundred Years of Bank of England Notes*, 1994. 246pp, beautifully illustrated. £35

■ British Academy, publisher, *Sylloge of Coins of the*

British Isles. 50 volumes, many still in print

■ Brooke, G C, *English Coins*, reprinted 1966. 300pp, 72 plates. An important one-volume guide to English coinage. SH

■ Challis, C, *A New History of the Royal Mint*, 1992. 806pp, 70 figures and maps. £95

■ Coincraft, publisher, *Standard Catalogue of English and UK Coins*, 1999. 741pp, fully illustrated. £19.50

■ Coincraft, publisher, *Standard Catalogue of the Coins of Scotland, Ireland, Channel Islands and Isle of Man*, 1999. 439pp, illustrated. £34.50

■ Cooper, D, *Coins and Minting*, Shire Publications number 106, 1996. 32pp, illustrated. £2.25. An excellent account of minting

■ Cooper, D, *The Art and Craft of Coinmaking*, 1988. 264pp, fully illustrated. £2.25. An excellent account of minting

■ Dolley, M, *Viking Coins in the Danelaw and Dublin*, 1965. 32pp, 16 plates. Excellent introductory handbook. SH

■ Dolley, M, *Anglo-Saxon Pennies*, reprint, 1970. 32pp, 16 plates. SH

■ Dolley, M, *The Norman Conquest and English Coinage*, 1966. 40pp, illustrated. SH

■ Dowle, A, and Finn, P, *The Guide Book to the Coinage of Ireland*, 1969. The first standard catalogue of Irish, still useful for information on patterns and proofs, good bibliography. SH

■ Dyer, G P, editor, *Royal Sovereign 1489-1989*, 1989. 99pp, fully illustrated. £30

■ Elias, E R D, *The Anglo-Gallic Coins*, 1984. 262pp, fully illustrated. £20. Essential for collectors of this series

■ Freeman, A, *The Moneyer and Mint in the Reign of Edward the Confessor 1042-1066*. Two parts, 1985. £40. A complete survey of the coinage of the reign

■ Frey, A R, *Dictionary of Numismatic Names*,

reprinted 1973. 405pp. The best numismatic dictionary, well worth searching for a second hand copy. SH
■ Grinsell, L V, *The History and Coinage of the Bristol Mint*, 1986. 60pp, illustrated. £5.
■ Grueber, H A, *Handbook of the Coins of Great Britain and Ireland*, revised edition, 1970. 272pp, 64 plates. A superb book. SH
■ Hobbs, R, *British Iron Age Coins in the British Museum*, 1996. 246pp, 137 plates. £40. Invaluable. Lists over 4,500 pieces
■ Holmes, R, *Scottish Coins, a History of Small Change in Scotland*, 1998. An invaluable guide to historic small change. 112pp, illustrated. £5.99
■ Holmes, N M McQ, *Scottish Coins in the Museums of Scotland, Part 1, 1526-1603*, 2006. 58pp, 99 plates. £55
■ de Jersey, P, *Celtic Coinage in Britain*, Shire Publications, 1996. 56pp, illustrated. £4.99
■ Linecar, H W A, *British Coin Designs and Designers*, 1977. 146pp, fully illustrated. SH
■ Linecar, H W A, *The Crown Pieces of Great Britain and the Commonwealth of Nations*, 1969. 102pp, fully illustrated. The only book dealing solely with all British crowns. SH
■ Linecar, H W A, editor, *The Milled Coinage of England 1662-1946*, reprinted 1976. 146pp, illustrated. A useful volume giving degrees of rarity. SH
■ Linecar, H W A, and Stone, A G, *English Proof and Pattern Crown-Size Pieces, 1658-1960*, 1968. 116pp, fully illustrated. An important book. SH
■ Manville, H E, and Robertson, T J, *Encyclopedia of British Numismatics, volume 1: British Numismatic Auction Catalogues from 1710 to the Present*, 1986. 420pp, illustrated. £25
■ Manville, H E, *Encyclopedia of British Numismatics, volume 2.1: Numismatic Guide to British and Irish Periodicals, 1731-1991*, 1993. 570pp, illustrated. £60

■ Manville, H E, *Encyclopedia of British Numismatics, volume 2.2: Numismatic Guide to British and Irish Periodicals, 1836-1995*, 1997. 634pp, 31 illustrations. £60. Important reference
■ Manville, H E, *Encyclopedia of British Numismatics volume 2.3: Numismatic Guide to British and Irish Printed Books, 1600-2004*, 2005. 291pp. £60
■ Manville, H E, *Tokens of the Industrial Revolution: Foreign Silver Coins Countermarked for Use in Great Britain, c1787-1828*. 308pp, 50 plates. £40. A highly important work
■ Marsh, M A, *The Gold Sovereign*, Jubilee edition, 2002. 136pp. £16.95
■ Marsh, M A, *The Gold Half-Sovereign*, 2nd edition, 2004. 119pp, 54 plates. £18.50
■ Mass, J P, *The J P Mass Collection: English Short Cross Coins, 1180-1247*, 2001. £50. 2,200 specimens from the author's collection
■ McCammon, A L T, *Currencies of the Anglo-Norman Isles*, 1984. 358pp, fully illustrated. £25. Essential for students and collectors
■ Mucha, M, *Hermitage Museum, St Petersburg, Part IV: English, Irish and Scottish Coins, 1066-1485*, 2005. 23 plates. £40.
■ North, J J, *English Hammered Coins, volume 1: Early Anglo-Saxon to Henry III, cAD600-1272*, 1994. 320pp, 20 plates. £35. Essential. A great reference for collectors
■ North, J J, *English Hammered Coins, volume 2: Edward I to Charles II, 1272-1662*, 1993. 224pp, 11 plates. £30. Essential. A great reference for collectors
■ North, J J, and Preston-Morley, P J, *The John G Brooker Collection: Coins of Charles I*, 1984. £19.50.
■ O'Sullivan, W, *The Earliest Irish Coinage*, 1981. 47pp, 4 plates. Deals with Hiberno-Norse coinage. SH
■ O'Sullivan, W, *The Earliest Anglo-Irish Coinage*, 1964. 88pp, 10 plates. Deals with

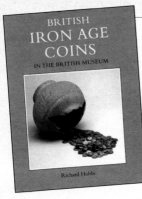

coinage from 1185-1216. Reprint available at £5. SH
■ Peck, C W, *English Copper, Tin and Bronze Coins in the British Museum, 1558-1958*, 1960. 648pp, 50 plates. Essential. The seminal work on the subject. SH
■ Pudill, R, and Eyre, C, *The Tribes and Coins of Celtic Britain*, 2005. 81pp, fully illustrated, price list included. £15
■ Rayner, P A, *English Silver Coins Since 1649*, 1992. 254pp, illustrated, 3rd edition. £19.95. Essential. 3,000 coins listed, 400 illustrated. Deals with varieties, rarities, patterns and proofs and mintage figures
■ Robinson, B, *Silver Pennies and Linden Towels: The Story of the Royal Maundy*, 1992. 274pp, 118 illustrations. £29.95. A very important work on the subject, entertaining
■ Spink, publisher, *Standard Catalogue of British Coins*, 2006. 41st edition. Fully illustrated. £25. After half a century still the first point of reference for English coin collectors
■ Spink, publisher, *Coins of Scotland, Ireland and the Islands*, 2003. 2nd edition. Illustrated. £25. An important addition to one's library
■ Stewart, I H, *The Scottish Coinage*, 1967. 2nd edition. 215pp, 22 plates. Long out of print, but still essential for the serious collector. SH
■ Sutherland, C H V, *English Coinage, 600-1900*, 1973. 232pp, 108 plates. Beautifully written and the best narrative account of coinage. SH
■ Thompson, J D A, *Inventory of British Coin Hoards, AD 600-1500*, 1956. 165pp, 24 plates. SH
■ Van Arsdell, R D, *Celtic Coinage of Britain*, 1989. 584pp, 54 plates, 80 maps. £40. A pioneering work causing much debate; important for the illustrations alone
■ Williams, J, *Money, A History*, 1997. 256pp, fully illustrated. £25. Accompanies the British Museum's HSBC Money Gallery opened in 1997
■ Wilson, A and Rasmussen, M, *English*

Pattern Trial and Proof Coins in Gold, 1547-1968, 2000. 537pp, illustrated. £85. Covers a fascinating series
■ Withers, P and B, *British Coin Weights*, 1993. A corpus of the coin-weights made for use in England, Scotland and Ireland. 366pp, illustrated. £95. For the serious student
■ Withers, P and B, *Farthings and Halfpennies, Edward I and II*, 2005. 60pp, illustrated. £10. Helpful series guide
■ Withers, P and B, *Farthings and Halfpennies, Edward III and Richard II*, 2002. Illustrated. £10
■ Withers, P and B, *Halfpennies and Farthings, Henry IV, V and VI*, 2003. 68pp, illustrated. £12
■ Withers, P and B, *Halfpennies and Farthings, Edward IV to Henry VII*, 2004. 56pp, illustrated. £12
■ Withers, P and B, *Small Silver, Henry VIII to the Commonwealth*, 2004. 56pp, illustrated. £12
■ Withers, P and B, *Irish Small Silver, John to Edward VI*, 2004. 56pp, illustrated. £12.
■ Withers, P and B, *The Galata Guide to the Pennies of Edward I and Edward II and the Coins of the Mint Berwick-upon-Tweed*, 2006. 64pp, fully illustrated. £20
■ Woodhead, P, *The Herbert Schneider Collection of English Gold Coins, Part 1: Henry III to Elizabeth I*, 1996. 466pp, 83 plates. £60. A great catalogue of the best collection in private hands, describes and illustrates 890 coins
■ Woodhead, P, *The Herbert Schneider Collection of English Gold Coins, Part 2: 1603 to 20th Century*, 2002. 58 plates. Essential like volume 1, it describes and illustrates 674 coins
■ Wren, C R, *The Voided Long Cross Coinage, 1247-1279*, 1993. 80pp, illustrated. £9
■ Wren, C R, *The Short Cross Coinage 1180-1247*, 1992. 90pp, illustrated. £8.75. Very good guide to identification with excellent drawings

Treasure truths

A rundown of the treasure laws as they apply to coins, and details of where collectors and finders can go for more information

On September 24, 1997, the Treasure Act 1996 came into force, replacing the old medieval law of treasure trove.

It widened the definition of finds that are treasure. In the past, before an object could be declared 'treasure' and therefore be the property of the Crown, it had to pass three tests: it had to be made substantially of gold or silver, it had to have been deliberately hidden with the intention of recovery and its owner or the heirs had to be unknown.

If then a museum wanted to keep the coins or artefacts, the lawful finder normally received the full market value; if not the coins were returned to the finder.

The new Act removes the need to establish that objects were hidden with intention of being recovered. It also sets out the precious metal content required for a find to qualify as treasure and extends the definition of treasure.

Treasure is: 'all coins that contain at least 10% gold or silver by weight of metal and that come from the same find, provided a find consists of at least two coins with gold or silver content of at least 10%. The coins must be at least 300 years old at the time

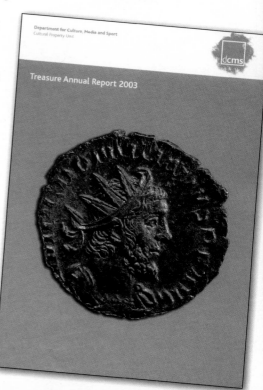

Department for Culture, Media and Sport
Cultural Property Unit

Treasure Annual Report 2003

dcms

The Treasure Valuation Committee

Under the 1996 Act the Treasure Valuation Committee replaced the Treasure Trove Reviewing Committee.

The committee commissions valuation reports from expert advisers.

All the interested parties (the finder, the landowner and the museum that intends to acquire the find) are given the chance to comment on these valuations or commission independent valuations of their own.

These reports are now delivered very quickly. The latest report, for 2003, deals with 425 finds

and is illustrated throughout in colour.

At present the committee is chaired by Professor Norman Palmer, a leading authority on the law of treasure trove.

The committee consists of Professor Norman Palmer; Dr Jack Ogden, National Association of Goldsmiths; Trevor Austin, President of the National Council for Metal Detecting; Dr Arthur MacGregor, Curator of Antiquities at the Ashmolean Museum; May Sinclair, a coin expert specialising in medieval coins at Spink; and Thomas Curtis, a specialist in ancient coins at Baldwin's.

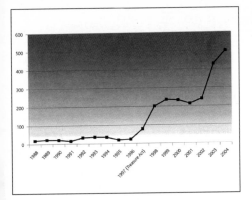

ABOVE: A graph from the 2003 Treasure Report shows a massive increase in reports of treasure since the 1997 Act came into force

of discovery. In the case of finds consisting of coins that contain less than 10% gold or silver there must be at least 10 such coins.'

The Act adds 'Single coins will not be treasure, unless they are found in association with objects that are treasure, or unless there is exceptionally strong evidence that they were buried with the intention of recovery (for example, a single coin found in plough soil without any sign of a container would not provide such evidence).'

As far as more modern coins are concerned, such as finds of guineas or sovereigns, the Act reads as follows: 'Only objects that are less than 300 years old, that are made substantially of gold or silver, that have been deliberately hidden with the intention of recovery and whose owners or heirs are unknown will come into this category.

'In practice such finds are rare and the only such discoveries that have been made within recent years have been hoards of gold and silver coins of the eighteenth, nineteenth or twentieth centuries.

'Single coins found on their own will not qualify under this provision, unless there is exceptionally strong evidence to show that they were buried with the intention of recovery: for example, a single coin found in plough soil without any sign of a container would not provide such.

'Therefore gold and silver objects that are clearly less than 300 years old need not be

reported unless the finder has reason to believe that they may have been deliberately hidden with the intention of recovery.'

The Act simplifies the task of coroners in determining whether or not a find is treasure, and it includes a new offence of non-declaration of treasure.

It also states that lawful occupiers and landowners have the right to be informed of finds of treasure from their land and that they will be eligible for reward.

However, following the Government's operational review of the Treasure Act, the definition of 'treasure' was extended to include:

■ any object (other than a coin), any part of which is base metal which, when found, is one of at least two base metal objects in the same find which are of prehistoric date.

■ any object (other than a coin), which is of prehistoric date, and any part of which is gold and silver.

A Treasure (Designation) Order came into force on January 1, 2003.

Information for finders & metal detectorists

Copies of *The Treasure Act 1966 Code of Practice (England & Wales) 1997*, can be obtained from the Department for Culture, Media and Sport.

This gives much useful information including a current list of coroners in the UK and a list of coins commonly found that contain less than 10 per cent of gold or silver. It also gives advice on the care of finds, identification and storage.

There is also a very useful leaflet entitled *The Treasure Act, information for finds of treasure*, which deals with everything in a question-and-answer way, for example:

■ What should I do if I find something that may be treasure?

■ How do I report a find of treasure?

■ What if I do not report a find of treasure?

■ How do I know that I will receive a fair price for my find?

Both these publications can be obtained free of charge from:
Department of Culture, Media and Sport, 2-4 Cockspur Street, London SW1Y 5DH.
Tel: 020 7211 6200.

42

Counterfeit coins

Forgeries have always been a problem. Here is some advice on the most commonly counterfeited coins and the methods used to make them

There have been forgeries since the earliest days of coin production, so, of course, new forgeries appear on the scene every year.

There is always someone willing to try to deceive the collector and the dealer.

However, nowadays, few forgers end up making much money.

As a result of the actions of the British Numismatic Trade Association, the trade is now tightly-knit and anxious to stamp out new forgeries before they have a chance to become a serious menace.

They were last a matter of major concern in the late 1960s and early 1970s, when an enormous number of 1887 £5 pieces and United States $20, manufactured in Beirut, came on to the market.

Also in the early 1970s, the Dennington forgeries could have made a serious impact on the English hammered gold market, but luckily they were detected early on. Unfortunately, a number of these are still in circulation.

In the late 1970s a crop of forgeries of Ancient British coins came to light, causing a panic in academic and trade circles.

This caused a lack of confidence in the trade and it took a number of years for the confidence to return. The BNTA follows

LEFT: Dennington forgeries: Edward III noble (top) and Mary Fine Sovereign

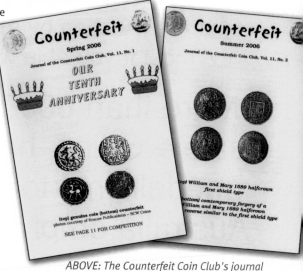

ABOVE: The Counterfeit Coin Club's journal

up any information about forgeries.

A spate of copies of Anglo-Saxon coins from the West Country were being sold as replicas in the early 1990s, but they are still deceptive in the wrong hands.

A list of them and was published in the IAPN Bulletin of Forgeries in 1995-96, volume 20, number 2.

The different types of forgery

Forgeries can be divided into two main groups: contemporary forgeries intended to be used as face-value money and forgeries intended to deceive collectors.

The following five methods of reproduction have been used:

■ Electrotyping. These copies would normally deceive an expert.

■ Casting. Old casts are easily recognisable, as they have marks made by air bubbles on the surface, and show a generally 'fuzzy' effect. Modern cast copies are much more of a problem.

They are produced by sophisticated 'pressure-casting', which can be extremely difficult to distinguish from the originals.

■ The fabrication of false dies. With hammered coins, counterfeits are not difficult for an expert to detect. However, the sophisticated die-production techniques used in Beirut have resulted in good forgeries of modern gold and silver coins.

■ The use of genuine dies put to illegal use, such as re-striking.

■ Alteration of a genuine coin, most commonly a George V penny. The 1933 is extremely rare, so other years are often altered to provide the rarer date.

Counterfeit Coin Club
There is a Counterfeit Coin Club that produces a small quarterly journal. For membership details write to its President: Ken Peters, 8 King's Road, Biggin Hill, Kent TN16 3XU. Tel: 01959 573686.

Worrying forgeries
Anthony Dennington was tried at the Central Criminal Court in the 1960s and found guilty of six charges of 'causing persons to pay money by falsely pretending that they were buying genuine antique coins'.

A small number of these pieces are still in the trade, and since they have deceived some collectors and dealers, we have recorded them here (right), as they appeared in the International Bureau for the Suppression of Counterfeit Coins Bulletin in August 1976.

These copies are generally very good and you must beware of them. The following points may be useful guidelines.

■ The coins are usually slightly 'shiny' in appearance, and the edges are not good, because they have been filed down and polished.

■ They are usually very 'hard' to touch, whereas there is a certain amount of 'spring' in the genuine articles.

■ They usually, but not always, feel slightly thick. They do not quite feel like an electrotype but are certainly thicker than normal.

■ Although the Mary Fine sovereign reproduction is heavier, at 16.1986g, these pieces are usually lighter in weight than the originals.

Modern coins
There has been a huge increase in well-produced forgeries of modern coins in the last 25 years.

They are so good it is often impossible for the naked eye to detect the difference, and it has become the job of the scientist and metallurgist.

BELOW: Modern cast copies of Anglo-Saxon pennies: Ceolwulf I above and Coenwulf below

Dennington forgeries still in the trade

■ Henry III gold penny
■ Edward III Treaty period noble
■ Edward III Treaty period noble with saltire before King's name
■ Henry IV heavy coinage noble
■ Henry V noble, Class C, mullet at King's sword arm
■ Henry VI mule noble
■ Henry VI noble, annulet issue, London
■ Edward IV royal, Norwich
■ Edward IV royal, York
■ Elizabeth I angel
■ Mary Fine sovereign 1553
■ James I unite, mintmark mullet
■ James I rose royal, third coinage, mint mark lis
■ James I third coinage laurel
■ Commonwealth unite 1651
■ Commonwealth half-unite 1651
■ Charles II touch piece

ABOVE: A counterfeit
from the 1950s. The last
of a series bearing dates
between 1902 to 1920, where
the original pattern piece was a genuine South
Africa sovereign from post-1924

Many of these pieces have deceived dealers and collectors.

This increase in the number of modern counterfeits has been due to the massive rise in coin values since the 1960s.

The vast majority of these modern forgeries emanate from the Middle East, where it is legal to produce counterfeits of other countries' coins. But the coin trade is alert and reports are circulated whenever a new forgery is spotted.

But with the profit a forger can make, no one should be complacent. It only takes about £350 worth of gold to make an 1887-dated £5 piece of correct composition, valued at around £750.

Detecting forgeries requires specialist knowledge, so we can only point out to you which coins are commonly counterfeited.

In the catalogue section of British Coins Market Values, we have placed (F) beside a number of coins which have been counterfeited and which frequently turn up.

You should watch out for sovereigns, of which there are forgeries of every date from 1900 to 1932 and recent dates such as 1957 and 1976.

Pieces you should be particularly careful about, especially if they are being offered below the normal catalogue value, are listed in the box.

Most modern forgeries of, for example, Gothic crowns, are offered at prices which are 10% or 20% below the current market price.

The moral is: if something looks too good to be true, it probably is!

Other safeguards against forgery
The best protection against purchasing forgeries is to buy your coins from a reputable dealer who is a member of the BNTA or the International Association of Professional Numismatists, or one who will unconditionally guarantee that all his coins are genuine.

Legal tender coins, which include £5 and £2 pieces, sovereigns, half sovereigns and crowns, are protected by the Forgery and Counterfeiting Act. Contact the police if you believe this Act may have been contravened.

If your dealer is unhelpful over a non-legal tender item which you have purchased, and which you think has been falsely described, you can take legal action under the Trades Description Act 1968. This is a long and difficult process. Contact your local Trading Standards Office or Consumer Protection department.

Literature on forgery
The back issues of Spink's Numismatic Circular and Seaby's Coin and Medal Bulletin are useful sources of information on the forgeries that have been recorded over the years.

The ISBCC also produced a series of important forgery bulletins, mainly on modern coins, which can now only be found secondhand.

The IAPN produce very good reports on forgeries for their own members.

The most useful work on hammered coins is by L A Lawrence in the British Numismatic Journal back in 1905! (Forgery in relation to Numismatics, BNJ 1905-1907).

Commonly forged coins

- 1738, 1739 two guineas
- 1793, 1798 guineas, there could also be other dates
- 1820 pattern £2
- 1839 £5, in particular the plain edge variety
- 1887 £5
- 1887 £2, many forgeries in circulation
- 1893 £5, £2
- 1902 £5, £2
- 1911 £5, £2
- 1817, 1819, 1822, 1825, 1827, 1887, 1889, 1892, 1892M, 1908C, 1913C sovereigns; 1900-1932 inclusive, plus 1957, 1959, 1963, 1966, 1967, 1974, 1976
- 1847 Gothic crowns
- 1905 halfcrowns

Bonhams
1793

inc. Glendinings

Coins at Auction

Bonhams incorporating Glendinings has been selling coins and medals at auction since the turn of the last century. Recent results have reflected the current buoyancy of the market, with high prices being achieved for quality items.

Coin Grading

IT IS MOST important that newcomers to collecting should get to know the various grades of condition before attempting to buy or sell coins.

The system of grading most commonly used in Britain recognises the following main classes in descending order of quality: Brilliant Uncirculated (B.Unc,BU), Uncirculated (Unc), Extremely Fine (EF), Very Fine (VF), Fine (F), Fair, Poor.

It is not surprising that beginners get confused at their first encounter with these grades. The word 'FINE' implies a coin of high quality, yet this grade turns out to be very near the bottom of the scale and is in fact about the lowest grade acceptable to most collectors of modern coinage in Britain.

American grading

It is not really necessary to go into the details of American grading here, since it is only on a very few occasions that a British collector will order the coins he wants directly from an American dealer. However, across the Atlantic their grading system is quite different from ours, and whilst it purports to be a lot more accurate, it is actually much more prone, in our opinion, to be abused, and we prefer the English dealers' more conservative methods of grading. American dealers use many more terms than we do, ranging from Mint State to About Good. The latter could be described as 'very heavily worn, with portions of lettering, date and legend worn smooth. The date may be partly legible'. In England we would simply say 'Poor'.

Numerical method

The other area which British collectors will find difficult to evaluate is the American numerical method of describing coins as, for example, MS 70, MS 65. The MS simply stands for Mint State and an MS 65 would be described as 'an above average Uncirculated coin which may be brilliant or lightly toned but has some surface marks'. The MS system seemed to be acceptable at first but there now appear to be two schools of thought in America and you will quite frequently see coins graded in the more traditional manner as well as the MS style in sale catalogues. Fortunately American grades have not come into use in this country, although dealers have followed the American manner of embellishing coin descriptions to make them more desirable, which is understandable and in many ways can be an improvement on the old method of saying simply that the coin is 'Fine', which, of course, might not do justice to it.

Full mint lustre

There are two schools of thought on the use of the terms Brilliant Uncirculated and Uncirculated. The former is often considered to be the most useful and descriptive term for coins of copper, bronze, nickel-brass or other base metals, which display what is known as 'full mint lustre'. When this term is being used it is often necessary in the same context to employ the grade Uncirculated to describe coins which have never been in circulation but have lost the original lustre of a newly minted coin. However, some dealers and collectors tend to classify as Uncirculated all coins which have not circulated, whether they are brilliant or toned, and do not use the term Brilliant Uncirculated.

Fleur de coin

Sometimes FDC (fleur de coin) is used to define top grade coins, but this really only applies to pieces in perfect mint state, having no flaws or surface scratches. With modern methods of minting, slight damage to the surface is inevitable, except in the case of proofs, and therefore Brilliant Uncirculated or Uncirculated best describe the highest grade of modern coins.

The word 'proof' should not be used to denote a coin's condition. Proofs are pieces struck on specially prepared blanks from highly polished dies and usually have a mirror-like finish.

Opinions differ

In all this matter of condition it might be said that the grade 'is in the eye of the beholder', and there are always likely to be differences of opinion as to the exact grade of a coin. Some collectors and dealers have tried to make the existing scale of definitions more exact by adding letters such as N (Nearly), G (Good, meaning slightly better than the grade to which the letter is added), A (About or Almost) and so on. To be still more accurate, in cases where a coin wears more on one side than the other, two grades are shown, the first for the obverse, the second for the reverse thus: GVF/EF.

Additional description

Any major faults not apparent from the use of a particular grade are often described separately. These include dents and noticeable scratches, discoloration, areas of corrosion, edge knocks, holes, on otherwise good quality pieces, and the like.

Middle range of grades

One should always look for wear on the highest points of the design, of course, but these vary from coin to coin. To present a comprehensive guide to exact grading one would have to illustrate every grade of every coin type in a given series, on the lines of the famous *Guide to the Grading of United States Coins*, by Brown and Dunn. This is a complete book in itself (over 200 pages) and obviously such a mammoth task could not be attempted in the space available here. Therefore, on the following page we present representative examples from three different periods in the British series, to illustrate the 'middle' range of coin conditions.

Still in mint state

We have already dealt with the grades BU and Unc; they both describe coins which are still in the state in which they left the Mint, and which have never passed into general circulation. They are likely to show minor scratches and edge knocks due to the mass handling processes of modern minting.

Fair and Poor

At the other end of the scale we have Fair, a grade that is applied to very worn coins which still have the main parts of the design distinguishable, and Poor which denotes a grade in which the design and rim are worn almost flat and few details are discernible.

Here we show (enlarged) examples of the grades EF, VF and F. On the left are hammered long cross pennies of Aethelred II; in the centre, from the later hammered series, are groats of Henry VIII; on the right are shillings of William IV.

Extremely Fine. This describes coins which have been put into circulation, but have received only the minimum of damage since. There may be a few slight marks or minute scratches in the field (flat area around the main design), but otherwise the coin should show very little sign of having been in circulation.

Very Fine. Coins in this condition show some amount of wear on the raised surfaces, but all other detail is still very clear. Here, all three coins have had a little wear as can be seen in the details of the hair and face. However, they are still in attractive condition from the collector's viewpoint.

Fine. In this grade coins show noticeable wear on the raised parts of the design; most other details should still be clear. The penny and the groat show a lot of wear over the whole surface. On the shilling the hair above the ear has worn flat.

Extremely Fine (EF)

Very Fine (VF)

Fine (F)

Abbreviations & Terms

used in the Market Price Guide section

* – Asterisks against some dates indicate that no firm prices were available at the time of going to press.

2mm – P of PENNY is 2mm from trident. On other 1895 pennies the space between is only 1mm.

AE – numismatic symbol for copper or copper alloys.

Arabic 1, Roman I – varieties of the 1 in 1887.

Arcs – decorative border of arcs which vary in number.

B (on William III coins) – minted at Bristol.

*1866 shilling lettered
BBITANNIAR in error*

BBITANNIAR – lettering error.

Bank of England – this issued overstruck Spanish dollars for currency use in Britain 1804-1811.

black – farthings 1897-1918, artificially darkened to avoid confusion with half sovereigns.

briit – lettering error.

B. Unc, BU – Brilliant Uncirculated condition.

C (on milled gold coins) – minted at Ottawa (Canada).

C (on William III coins) – minted at Chester.

close colon – colon close to DEF.

crosslet 4 – having upper and lower serifs to horizontal bar of 4 (see plain 4).

cu-ni – cupro-nickel.

dashes (thus –) following dates in the price list indicate that some particular characteristic of a coin is the same as that last described. Two dashes mean that two characters are repeated, and so on.

debased – in 1920 the silver fineness in British coins was debased from .925 to .500.

diag – diagonal.

'Dorrien and Magens' – issue of shillings by a group of bankers. Suppressed on the day of issue.

DRITANNIAR – lettering error.

E (on William III coins) – minted at Exeter.

E, E* (on Queen Anne coins) – minted at Edinburgh.

Edin – Edinburgh.

EEC – European Economic Community.

EF (over price column) – Extremely Fine condition.

E.I.C. – East India Co (supplier of metal).

Elephant and castle

eleph, eleph & castle – elephant or elephant and castle provenance mark (below the bust) taken from the badge of the African ('Guinea') Company, which imported the metal for the coins.

Eng – English shilling. In 1937, English and Scottish versions of the shilling were introduced. English versions: lion standing on crown (1937-1951); three leopards on a shield (1953-66).

exergue – segment below main design, usually containing the date.

*On this penny the exergue is the
area containing the date*

ext – extremely.

F – face value only.

F (over price column) – Fine condition.

(F) – forgeries exist of these pieces. In some cases the forgeries are complete fakes, in others where the date is rare the date of a common coin has been altered. Collectors are advised to be very cautious when buying any of these coins.

Fair – rather worn condition.

Fantasies – non-currency items, often just produced for the benefit of collectors.

far colon – colon father from DEF than in close colon variety.

FDC – Fleur de coin. A term used to describe coins in perfect mint condition, with no flaws, scratches or other marks.

fig(s) – figure(s).

fillet – hair band.

flan – blank for a coin or medal.

GEOE – lettering error.

*Florin of Victoria with the design in
the Gothic style*

Gothic – Victorian coins featuring Gothic-style portrait and lettering.

guinea-head – die used for obverse of guinea.

H – mintmark of The Mint, Birmingham, Ltd.

hd – head.

hp, harp (early, ord etc.) – varieties of the Irish harp on reverse.

hearts – motif in top RH corner of Hanoverian shield on reverse.

illust – illustration, or illustrated.

im – initial mark.

inc, incuse – incised, sunk in.

inv – inverted.

JH – Jubilee Head.

*The Jubilee Head was introduced
on the coinage in 1887 to mark
Victoria's Golden Jubilee*

KN – mintmark of the Kings Norton Metal Co Ltd.

L.C.W. – Initials of Leonard Charles Wyon, engraver.

lge – large.

LIMA – coins bearing this word were struck from bullion captured by British ships from foreign vessels carrying South American treasure, some of which may have come from Peru (capital Lima).

1902 pennies showing the low horizon variety (A) and the normal horizon (B)

low horizon – on normal coins the horizon meets the point where Britannia's left leg crosses behind the right. On this variety the horizon is lower.
LVIII etc – regnal year in Roman numerals on the edge.
matt – type of proof without mirror-like finish.
M (on gold coins) – minted at Melbourne (Australia).
'military' – popular name for the 1813 guinea struck for the payment of troops fighting in the Napoleonic Wars.
mm – mintmark.
Mod eff – modified effigy of George V.
mule – coin struck from wrongly paired dies.
N (on William III coins) – minted at Norwich.

William III shilling with N (for Norwich mint) below the bust

no. – number.
obv – obverse, usually the 'head' side of a coin.
OH – Old Head.
ord – ordinary.
OT – ornamental trident.
P (on gold coins) – minted at Perth (Australia).
pattern – trial piece not issued for currency.

piedfort – a coin which has been specially struck on a thicker than normal blank. In France, whence the term originates, the Kings seem to have issued them as presentation pieces from the 12th century onwards. In Britain medieval and Tudor examples are known, and their issue has now been reintroduced by the Royal Mint, starting with the 20 pence piedfort of 1982.
plain (on silver coins) – no provenance marks in angles between shields on reverse.
plain 4 – with upper serif only to horizontal bar of 4 (see crosslet 4).
pln edge prf – plain edge proof.
plume(s) – symbol denoting Welsh mines as source of metal.
proof, prf – coin specially struck from highly polished dies. Usually has a mirror-like surface.
prov, provenance – a provenance mark on a coin (e.g. rose, plume, elephant) indicates the supplier of the bullion from which the coin was struck.
PT – plain trident.
raised – in relief, not incuse.
RB – round beads in border.
rev – reverse, 'tail' side of coin.
r – right.
r & p – roses and plumes.

Roses and plumes provenance marks

rose – symbol denoting west of England mines as source of metal.
RRITANNIAR – lettering error.
rsd – raised.
S (on gold coins) – minted at Sydney (Australia).
SA (on gold coins) – minted at Pretoria (South Africa).

Scottish shilling 1953-66

Scot – Scottish shilling. Lion seated on crown, holding sword and sceptre (1937-51); lion rampant, on shield (1953-66).
SS C – South Sea Company (source of metal).

1723 shilling bearing the South Sea Company's initials

SEC – SECUNDO, regnal year (on edge).
sh – shield(s).
sm – small.
'spade' – refers to spadelike shape of shield on George III gold coins.

'Spade' guinea, reverse

TB – toothed beads in border.
TER – TERTIO, regnal year (on edge).
trnctn, truncation – base of head or bust where the neck or shoulders terminate.
Unc – Uncirculated condition.
var – variety.
VF – Very Fine condition.
VIGO – struck from bullion captured in Vigo Bay.
VIP – 'very important person'. The so-called VIP crowns were the true proofs for the years of issue. Probably most of the limited number struck would have been presented to high ranking officials.
W.C.C. – Welsh Copper Co (supplier of metal).
wire type – figure of value in thin wire-like script.
W.W. – initials of William Wyon, engraver.
xxri – lettering error.
y, Y (on William III coins) – minted at York.
YH – Young Head.

Victoria Young Head Maundy fourpence

St James's Auctions

Auctions 6 and 7 will take place in the spring and autumn of 2007 at the Cavendish Hotel, 81 Jermyn Street, St James's, London SW1

We are currently accepting consignments for these sales

If you have items which you wish to sell, either individual coins or entire collections, we shall be accepting lots for Auction 6 until 31st January 2007 and for Auction 7 until 31st July 2007.

Commissions are often negotiable and, if the collection warrants it, commission can be agreed at 0%. Add to this our 0% insurance charge and our free photography and that means that 100% of hammer price goes to the consignor. If you wish to discuss this further, please contact us at the address below:

St James's Auctions
(Knightsbridge Coins / S C Fenton)
43 Duke Street, St James's
London SW1Y 6DD
Phone: 020 7930 7597 / 7888 / 8215
Fax: 020 7930 8214

British Coin Prices

CELTIC COINAGE

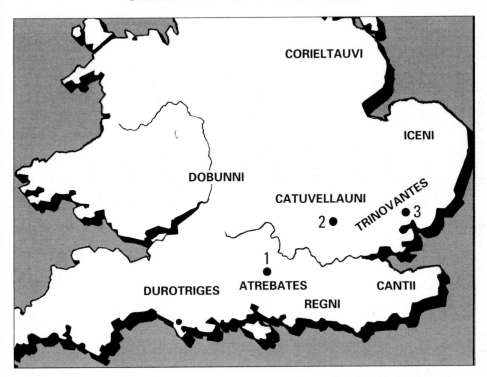

The distribution of the tribes in Britain based on the map in 'The coinage of Ancient Britain', by R.P. Mack, published by Spink and Son Ltd and B.A. Seaby Ltd.

Key to towns:
1. Calleva Atrebatum (Silchester)
2. Verulamium (St Albans)
3. Camulodunum (Colchester)

It is always difficult to produce a priced catalogue of coins, but none is more difficult than the early British series. The market has developed considerably since the publication of R.D. Van Arsdell's *Celtic Coinage of Britain*, which is an essential book for collectors (584 pages, 54 plates and many other illustrations, maps and diagrams).

A word of caution, though; quite a number of forgeries exist, some of relatively recent production, and unfortunately also numerous items from undeclared hoards are on the market, which makes it essential to buy from a reputable dealer.

We are very grateful for the help of Robert Van Arsdell since he produced the synopsis of the material which we have used. We have kept this very basic, and simply linked it up for easy reference with *The Coinage of Ancient Britain* by R. P. Mack, third edition, London 1975 (now out of print), and with the *British Museum Catalogue of British Iron Age Coins* by R. Hobbs, where it is possible. In the following lists Mack types are indicated by 'M' and BMC types by 'B'. The V numbers relate to the Van Arsdell catalogue. The existence of forgeries is indicated by **(F)**.

CELTIC COINAGE

Gold staters without legends

AMBIANI

	F	VF
Large flan type M1, 3, V10, 12	£500	£2250

Ambiani large flan type

		F	VF
Defaced die type M5, 7, V30, 33 ...	£300	£1000
Abstract type M26, 30, V44, 46	£300	£700
Gallic War type M27, a, V50, 52 **(F)** ...	£135	£300

Gallic War gold stater

SUESSIONES

	F	VF
Abstract type M34a, V85	£275	£800

VE MONOGRAM

	F	VF
M82, a, b, V87 **(F)**	£275	£750

WESTERHAM

	F	VF
M28, 29, V200, 202 , B1-24	£200	£450

Chute Gold Starter, V1205

CHUTE

	F	VF
M32, V1205, B35-76 **(F)**	£145	£300

CLACTON

	F	VF
Type I M47, V1458, B137-144	£300	£900
Type II M46, a, V30, 1455, B145-179	£325	£900

CORIELTAUVI

	F	VF
Scyphate type M—, V—, B3187-93	£250	£700

CORIELTAUVI (N.E. COAST TYPE)

	F	VF
Type I M50-51a, V800, B182-191 ...	£200	£450
Type II M52-57, S27, V804	£190	£425

Norfolk Wolf stater VA610-3

NORFOLK

	F	VF
Wolf type M49, a, b, V610, B212-278	£200	£450

CORIELTAUVI

	F	VF
South Ferriby Kite & Domino type, M449-450a, V.811, B3146-3186	£225	£525

Coritani (South Ferriby)

WHADDON CHASE

	F	VF
M133-138, V1470-1478, B279-350 **(F)**	£200	£500
Middle , Late Whaddon Chase V1485-1509	£225	£600

Whaddon Chase stater

WONERSH

	F	VF
M147, 148, V1522, B351-56	£325	£900

WEALD

	F	VF
M84, 229, V144, 150, B2466-68	£450	£1250

ICENI

	F	VF
Freckenham Type I M397-399, 403b, V620, B3384-95	£275	£600
Freckenham Type II M401, 2, 3a, 3c, V626, B3396-3419	£275	£625
Snettisham Type M—, V—, B3353-83	£300	£800

Iceni gold stater

ATREBATIC

	F	VF
M58-61, V210-216, B445-76	£200	£425

Atrebatic stater

Verica gold stater

	F	VF
SAVERNAKE FOREST M62, V1526, B359-64	£225	£550
DOBUNNIC M374, V1005, B2937-40	£350	£850

Gold quarter staters without legends

	F	VF
AMBIANI Large flan type M2, 4, V15, 20 **(F)**	£235	£675
Defaced die type M6, 8, V35, 37	£200	£525
GEOMETRIC M37, 39, 41, 41A, 42, V65, 146, 69, 67	£75	£175
SUSSEX M40, 43-45, V143, 1225-1229	£75	£175
VE MONOGRAM M83, V87 **(F)**	£150	£350

Atrebatic quarter stater, Bognor Cog Wheel

ATREBATIC M63-67, 69-75, V220-256, B478-546	£135	£325

Caesar's trophy, quarter stater VA145

KENTISH Caesar's Trophy type V145	£125	£300

Gold staters with legends

	F	VF
COMMIUS M92, V350, B724-730	£325	£900
TINCOMARUS M93, 93, V362, 363, B761-74	£450	£1250
VERICA Equestrian type M121, V500, B1143-58	£250	£600
Vine leaf type M125, V520, B1159-76	£275	£675

	F	VF
EPATICCUS M262, V575, B2021-23	£825	£2250
DUBNOVELLAUNUS In Kent M283, V176, B2492-98	£325	£825
In Essex M275, V1650, B2425-40 ...	£300	£800
EPPILLUS In Kent M300-1, V430, B1125-28 ...	£1250	£4000
ADDEDOMAROS (THREE TYPES) M266, 7, V1605, B2390-94 **(F)**	£200	£550
TASCIOVANUS Bucranium M149, V1680, B1591-1607 **(F)**	£350	£950

VOLISIOS DUMNOCOVEROS

Equestrian M154-7, V1730-1736, B1608-13	£300	£850
TASCIO/RICON M184, V1780, B1625-36	£600	£1500
SEGO M194, V1845, B1625-27	£1500	£4000
ANDOCO M197, V1860, B2011-14	£525	£1350

Tasciovanus Celtic Warrior

Cunobeline Gold Stater, V1910

CELTIC COINAGE

CUNOBELINE	F	VF
Two horses M201, V1910, B1769-71	£675	£1750
Corn ear M203 etc. V2010,		
B1772-1835 **(F)**	£275	£600

ANDOCO Stater

ANTED of the Dobunni		
M385-6, V1062-1066, B3023-27 **(F)**	£475	£1350
EISU		
M388, V1105, B3039-42 **(F)**	£525	£1500
INAM		
M390, V1140, B3056 **(F)**	extremely rare	
CATTI		
M391, V1130, B3057-60 **(F)**	£450	£1200
COMUX		
M392, V1092, B3061-63 **(F)**	£800	£2250
CORIO		
M393, V1035, B3064-3133 ... ... -	£450	£1200
BODVOC		
M395, V1052, B3135-42 **(F)**	£800	£2250

Bodvoc

VEP CORF		
M459-460, V940, 930, B3296-3300 **(F)**	£400	£900
DUMNOC TIGIR SENO		
M461, V972, B3325-27 **(F)**	£625	£1500
VOLISIOS DUMNOCOVEROS		
M463, V978, B3330-36	£450	£950

Cunobeline quarter stater V.1913-1

Gold quarter staters with legends

TINCOMARUS		
Abstract type M95, V365	£165	£350
Medusa head type M97, V387,		
B811-24	£200	£500
Tablet type M101-4, V387-390,		
B825-79	£125	£300

Tincommius Medusa head gold quarter stater

EPPILLUS	F	VF
CALLEVA M107, V407, B986-1015 ...	£125	£300

Eppillus CALLEVA type

VERICA		
Horse type M111-114, V465-468,		
B1143-46	£125	£275
TASCIOVANUS		
Horse type M152-3, V1690,1692,		
B1641-1650	£125	£275
CUNOBELINE		
Various types, B1836-55 from	£135	£275

Silver coins without legends

DUROTRIGES		
Silver stater M317, V1235,		
B2525-2731 **(F)**	£45	£125
Geometric type M319, V1242,		
B2734-79	£30	£90
Starfish type M320, V1270,		
B2780-81	£60	£200

Starfish Unit

DOBUNNIC		
Face M374a, b, 5, 6, 8, V1020,		
B2950-3000	£35	£100
Abstract M378a-384d, V1042,		
B3012-22	£30	£80

Corieltauvi, showing boar and horse

CORIELTAUVI		
Boar type M405a, V855, B3194-3250	£50	£160
South Ferriby M410 etc, V875	£40	£110

Iceni Unit, V730

CENI	F	VF
Boar type M407-9, V655-659, B3440-3511	£25	£75
Wreath type M414, 5, 440, V679, 675, B3763-74	£25	£80
Face type M412-413e, V665, B3536-55	£85	£275

QUEEN BOUDICA

	F	VF
Face type M413, 413D, V790, 792, B3556-3759	£45	£150

Silver coins of Boudica (left) and Commius (right)

COMMIUS

	F	VF
Head left M446b, V355, 357, B731-58	£45	£150

Silver coins with legends

EPPILLUS	F	VF
CALLEVA type M108, V415, B1016-1115	£45	£130

EPATICCUS		
Eagle type M263, V580, B2024-2289	£30	£90
Victory type M263a, V581, B2294-2328	£35	£100

Verica, Lion type unit V505

VERICA

	F	VF
Lim type M123, V505, B1332-59 ...	£40	£135

Silver unit, Epaticcus

CARATACUS

	F	VF
Eagle Type M265, V593, B2376-2384 (F)	£125	£325

TASCIOVANUS

Equestrian M158, V1745, B1667-68	£80	£275
VER type M161, V1699, B1670-73 ...	£80	£275

CUNOBELINE

Equestrian M216-8, 6, V1951, 1953, 2047, B1862	£90	£275
Bust right M236, VA2055, B1871-73	£80	£250

ANTED of the Dobunni

M387, V1082, B3032-38	£60	£150

EISU

M389, V1110, B3043-55	£45	£125

CELTIC COINAGE

BODVOC	F	VF
M396, V1057, B3143-45 (F)	£125	£400

ANTED of the Iceni
M419-421, V710, 711, 715,		
B3791-4009	£30	£70

ECEN
| M424, V730, B4033-4215 ... ... | £25 | £65 |

EDNAM
| M423, 425b, V740, 734, B4219-4281 | £30 | £65 |

ECE
M425a, 426, 7, 8, V761, 764,		
762, 766, B4348-4538	£25	£60

AESU
| M432, V775, B4558-72 ... ... | £50 | £125 |

PRASUTAGUS
King of the Iceni (husband of Boudica),		
B4577-4580	£600	£1750

ESUP ASU
| M4566, VA924, B3272 ... ... | £75 | £250 |

VEP CORF
M460b, 464, V394, 950, B3277-3382,		
B3305-3314	£50	£100

DUMNOC TIGIR SENO
| M462, V974 B3328-3329 ... ... | £150 | £500 |

VOLISIOS DUMNOCOVEROS
| M463a, V978, 980, B3339 ... ... | £165 | £500 |

ALE SCA
| M469, V996 ... ... | £125 | £375 |

Bronze, base metal coins without legends

POTIN	F	VF
Experimental type M22a, V104	£35	£85

Potin coin class II

Class I M9-22, V122-131	£30	£75
Class II M23-25, V136-139	£30	£75
Thurrock Types V1402-1442	£35	£110

ARMORICAN	F	V
Billon stater	£30	£1
Billon quarter stater	£50	£1:

DUROTRIGES
Bronze stater M318, V1290	£20	£
Cast type M332-370, V1322-1370 ...	£35	£1

NORTH THAMES
M273, 274, 281, V1646 1615, 1669	£35	£1

NORTH KENT
M295, 296, V154	£65	£2

Bronze coins with legends

DUBNOVELLAUNUS in Essex
M277, 8, V1665, 1667	£60	£2

TASCIOVANUS
Head, beard M168, 9, V1707	£45	£1
VERLAMIO M172, V1808	£45	£1
Head, VER M177, V1816	£50	£2
Boar, VER M179, V1713	£50	£2
Equestrian M190, V1892	£75	£3
Centaur M192, V1882	£100	£4

ANDOCO
M200, V1871	£65	£2:

CUNOBELINE
Victory, TASC M221, V1971	£40	£1
Victory, CUN M22, a, V1973	£45	£1:
Winged animal, M225, V2081	£45	£1

Cunobeline bronze with Centaur reverse

Head, beard, M226, 9, V2131, 2085	£40	£1
Panel, sphinx, M230, V1977	£45	£1:
Winged beast, M231, V1979	£45	£1
Centaur, M242, V2089	£40	£1
Sow, M243, V2091	£40	£1
Warrior, M244, V2093	£35	£1
Boar, TASC, M245, V1983	£45	£1:
Bull, TASC M246, V2095	£40	£1
Metal worker, M248, V2097	£40	£1!
Pegasus, M249, V2099	£35	£1:
Horse, CAMV, M250, V2101	£45	£1:
Jupiter, horse, M251, V2103	£45	£1:
Janus head, M252, V2105	£50	£1
Jupiter, lion, M253, V1207	£40	£1
Sphinx, fig, M260, a, V2109	£60	£1

ENGLISH HAMMERED
Gold from 1344 and Silver from *circa* 600

Prices in this section are approximately what collectors can expect to pay for the commonest types of the coins listed; for most other types prices will range upwards from these amounts. Precise valuations cannot be given since they vary from dealer to dealer and, in any case, have to be determined by consideration of a number of factors e.g., the coin's condition (which is of prime importance in deciding its value).

For more detailed information refer to English Hammered Coins, Volumes 1 and 2, by J. J. North and published by Spink and Son Ltd. Any serious collectors should also obtain The Herbert Schneider Collection, Volume One, English Gold Coins 1257-1603, published by Spink and Son, 1996 and Volume Two English Gold Coins 1603 to 20th century, published by Spink and Son, 2002.

GOLD COINS
The Plantagenet Kings

Henry III gold penny

HENRY III 1216-1272   F   VF
Gold Penny
This specimen sold for £159,500 (including buyers premium) at a Spink auction on 9 July 1996. ext. rare

Edward III quarter noble

EDWARD III 1327-77
Third coinage

	F	VF
Florins or Double leopard	ext. rare	
Half florins or leopard...	ext. rare	
Quarter florins or helms	ext. rare	
Nobles ... ... from	£1250	£3250
Half nobles ... ... from	£1100	£3250
Quarter nobles	£400	£900

Fourth coinage
Pre-treaty with France (i.e. before 1315) with French title

	F	VF
Nobles	£600	£1400
Half nobles	£450	£1000
Quarter nobles	£225	£525

Transitional treaty period, 1361. Aquitaine title added

	F	VF
Nobles	£625	£1600
Half nobles	£350	£800
Quarter nobles	£200	£400

Edward III 1327-1377, Half noble, Transitional Treaty

Treaty period 1361-9 omit FRANC

	F	VF
Nobles, London	£625	£1450
Nobles, Calais		
(C in centre of rev.)	£650	£1500
Half nobles, London	£400	£850
Half nobles, Calais	£650	£1600
Quarter nobles, London	£200	£450
Quarter nobles, Calais	£225	£525

Post-treaty period 1369-77 French title resumed

	F	VF
Nobles, London	£650	£1600
Nobles, Calais		
(flag at stern or C in centre)	£675	£1650
Half nobles, London	£1000	£3000
Half nobles, Calais	£950	£2500

There are many other issues and varieties in this reign. These prices relate to the commoner pieces.

Richard II London half noble

RICHARD II 1377-99

	F	VF
Nobles, London	£750	£1700
Nobles, Calais		
(flag at stern)	£800	£1750
Half nobles, London	£900	£2750

HAMMERED GOLD

	F	VF
Half nobles, Calais		
(flag at stern)	£1250	£3500
Quarter nobles, London	£400	£900

There are many different varieties and different styles of lettering.

HENRY IV 1399-1413
Heavy coinage

	F	VF
Nobles (120grs) London	£4250	£13500
Nobles, Calais (flag at stern)	£4500	£15000
Half nobles, London	£4000	*
Half nobles, Calais	£4500	*
Quarter nobles, London	£1000	£2500
Quarter nobles, Calais	£1250	£3250

Light coinage

	F	VF
Nobles (108grs)	£1500	£4000
Half nobles	£2000	£5000
Quarter nobles	£625	£1200

Henry V noble

HENRY V 1413-22

	F	VF
Nobles, many varieties, from	£700	£1750
Half nobles	£650	£1500
Quarter nobles	£325	£650

This reign sees an increase in the use of privy marks to differentiate issues.

Henry VI noble, Annulet issue

HENRY VI 1422-61
Annulet issue (1422-27)

	F	VF
Nobles, London	£650	£1500
Nobles, Calais (flag at stern)	£700	£1650
Nobles, York	£950	£2500
Half nobles, London	£475	£1200
Half nobles, Calais	£750	£2000
Half nobles, York	£950	£2750
Quarter nobles, London	£225	£475
Quarter nobles, Calais	£250	£550
Quarter nobles, York	£275	£650

Henry VI, Quarter-Noble, Annulet issue

Rosette-mascle issue 1427-30	F	VF
Nobles, London	£1100	£300
Nobles, Calais	£1350	£350
Half nobles, London	£1500	£400
Half nobles, Calais	£1600	£450
Quarter nobles, London	£625	£125
Quarter nobles, Calais	£675	£150

Pinecone-mascle issue 1430-4

Nobles, London	£1050	£285
Half nobles, London	£1850	£500
Quarter noble	£750	£175

Henry VI quarter noble, leaf-mascle

Leaf-mascle issue 1434-5

Nobles	£2250	£600
Half nobles	£2000	£550
Quarter nobles	£875	£200

Leaf-trefoil issue 1435-8

Nobles	£2250	£600
Quarter noble	£875	£280

Trefoil issue 1438-43

Nobles	£2250	£650

Henry VI Gold Noble, Pinecone-mascle, London

Leaf-pellet issue 1445-54

Nobles	£2250	£600

Cross-pellet issue 1454-60

Nobles	£2500	£750

EDWARD IV 1st reign 1461-70
Heavy coinage 1461-64/5

Nobles (108grs)	£2500	£750
Quarter noble		ext. rare

Edward IV noble, heavy coinage

	F	VF
HENRY VI (restored) 1470-71		
Angels, London	£1200	£3250
Angels, Bristol (B in waves)	£1450	£4500
Half angels, London	£2000	£5000
Half angels, Bristol (B in waves) ...	£3500	*
EDWARD IV 2nd reign 1471-83		
Angels, London	£575	£1200
Angels, Bristol (B in waves)	£1750	£4000
Half angels, some varieties	£475	£1100
EDWARD IV or V 1483		
mm halved sun and rose		
Angels	£2000	£6500
Half angels	£3000	*
RICHARD III 1483-85		
Angel, reading **EDWARD**, *mm* boar's head on obverse, halved sun and rose on reverse	£4500	£10000
Angels, reading **RICHARD or RICAD**	£1850	£5000
Half angels	£4000	*

Edward IV Light Coinage 1464-70, Ryal, York

Light coinage 1464-70	F	VF
Ryals or rose nobles (120grs),		
London	£625	£1450
Flemish copy	£375	£800

Gold Angel, mm boar's head on obverse, and halved sun and rose on reverse

The Tudor Monarchs

	F	VF
Ryals, Bristol (B in waves)	£725	£1650
Ryals, Coventry (C in waves))	£1350	£3250
Ryals, Norwich (N in waves)	£1450	£3500
Ryals, York (E in waves)	£675	£1650
Half ryals, London	£525	£1250
Half ryals, Bristol (B in waves) ...	£825	£2250
Half ryals, Coventry (C in waves) ...	£3000	£8250
Half ryals Norwich (N in waves) ...	£2750	£7500
Half ryals, York (E in waves)	£575	£1500
Quarter ryals	£325	£750
Angels	£4500	*

Henry VII sovereign

	F	VF
HENRY VII 1485-1509		
Sovereigns of 20 shillings (all ext. rare) from	£13500	£40000
Ryals	£12500	£37500
Angels, varieties, different *mm* from	£525	£1250
Half angels	£475	1100

Edward IV angel, first reign

HAMMERED GOLD

Henry VII 1485-1509, Angel with Mint Mark pheon

HENRY VIII 1509-47

First coinage 1509-26

	F	VF
Sovereigns of 20 shillings *mm*		
crowned portcullis only	£6500	£17500
Angels (6s 8d) ... ... from	£525	£1200
Half angels	£475	£1100

Second coinage 1526-44

	F	VF
Sovereigns of 22s 6d, various *mm* ...	£6000	£15000
Angels (7s 6d)	£725	£1850
Half angels lis	£825	£2000
George-nobles *mm* rose	£5750	£18000
Half-George noble	£6000	*
Crowns of the rose *mm* rose	£4500	*
Crowns of the double-rose		
HK (Henry and Katherine of Aragon)	£525	£1100
HA (Henry and Anne Boleyn) ...	£825	£2250
HI (Henry and Jane Seymour) ...	£575	£1350
HR (HENRICUS REX)	£525	£1100
Halfcrowns of the double-rose		
HK	£425	£975
HI	£525	£1250
HR	£625	£1350

Third coinage 1544-47

	F	VF
Sovereigns of 20s, London ... from	£3750	£11000
Sovereigns of 20s, Southwark	£3500	£10000
Sovereigns of 20s, Bristol	£4250	£12500
Half sovereigns, London	£650	£1650
Half sovereigns, Southwark	£675	£1750
Half sovereigns, Bristol	£1200	£3500

*Henry VIII Angel, 3rd coinage with mint mark lis
(shown slightly enlarged)*

Angels	£525	£1100
Half angels	£475	£1000
Quarter angels	£425	£950
Crowns, HENRIC 8, London	£500	£1000
Crowns, Southwark	£575	£1350
Crowns, Bristol	£550	£1250

	F	VF
Halfcrowns, London	£400	£90
Halfcrowns, Southwark	£425	£9
Halfcrowns, Bristol	£475	£12

EDWARD VI 1547-53

Posthumous coinage in name of Henry VIII (1547-51)

	F	VF
Sovereigns, London	£5250	£130
Sovereigns, Bristol	£5500	£140
Half sovereigns, London	£575	£16
Half sovereigns, Southwark	£600	£16
Crowns, London	£525	£12
Crowns, Southwark	£550	£13
Halfcrowns, London	£475	£11
Halfcrowns, Southwark	£450	£10

Coinage in Edward's own name

First period 1547-49

	F	VF
Half sovereigns, Tower, read EDWARD 6	£1350	£425

*Edward VI sovereign, posthumous coinage
(not actual size)*

	F	VF
Half sovereigns, Southwark	£1250	£400
Crown	£2500	
Halfcrowns	£2000	

Second period 1549-50

	F	VF
Sovereigns	£3750	£1000
Half sovereigns, uncrowned bust		
London	£3250	
Half sovereigns, SCUTUM on obv. ...	£1350	£365
Half sovereigns, Durham House		
MDXL VII	£4500	
Half sovereigns, crowned bust,		
London	£1250	£350
Half sovereigns, half-length bust,		
Durham House	£4250	
Crowns, uncrowned bust	£1200	£325
Crowns, crowned bust	£1200	£300
Halfcrowns, uncrowned bust	£1200	£300
Halfcrowns, crowned bust	£1000	£275

*Edward VI fine sovereign of 30s third period with mint
mark ostrich head*

Edward VI Sovereign of 0 Shillings. Third Period

Third period 1550-53	F	VF
'Fine' sovereigns of 30s, king enthroned	£16500	£47500
Sovereigns of 20s, half-length figure ..	£2500	£7000
Half sovereigns, similar to last	£1350	£3500
Crowns, similar but SCUTUM on rev ..	£1200	£3000
Halfcrowns, similar	£1350	£3500
Angels	£5750	£17500
Half angel	ext. rare	

MARY 1553-4

	F	VF
Sovereigns, different dates, some undated, some *mms*	£3000	£8000
Ryals, dated MDUI (1553)	£10000	£37500
Angels, *mm* pomegranate	£1350	£3000
Half angels	£2750	£6500

Mary Gold Sovereign of 1553

HAMMERED GOLD

PHILIP AND MARY 1554-8	F	VF
Angels, *mm* lis	£3000	£8000
Half angels	£6500	*

Philip and Mary angel

Elizabeth I 1558-1603
Hammered issues

	F	VF
'Fine' sovereigns of 30s, different issues from	£3000	£8000
Ryals	£9000	£25000
Angels, different issues	£675	£1750
Half angels	£650	£1600
Quarter angels	£575	£1350

Elizabeth I quarter angel

	F	VF
Pounds of 20 shillings, different mint marks from	£1750	£4500
Half pounds, different issues	£1250	£3000
Crowns —	£900	£2000
Halfcrowns —	£750	£1850

Elizabeth I hammered halfcrown

Milled issues

Half pounds, one issue but different		
marks	£1850	£5250
Crowns —	£1650	£4500
Halfcrowns —	£2000	£5750

The Stuart Kings

James I gold Spur-ryal

James I Thistle crown

3rd coinage 1619-25

	F	VF
Rose-ryals, varieties	£2250	£5750
Spur-ryals	£3250	£8000
Angels	£1000	£2750
Laurels, different busts	£525	£800
Half Laurels	£375	£800
Quarter laurels	£225	£500

James I laurel

JAMES I 1603-25
1st coinage 1603-4

	F	VF
Sovereigns of 20 shillings two bust	£1500	£4500
Half sovereigns	£2250	£7000
Crowns	£1500	£4000
Halfcrowns	£675	£1500

2nd coinage 1604-19

	F	VF
Rose-ryals of 30 shillings	£2000	£4850
Spur-ryals of 15 shillings	£3500	£9500
Angels	£750	£2000
Half angels	£1850	£5000
Unites, different busts	£525	£1100
Double crowns —	£375	£800
Britain crowns —	£225	£525

CHARLES I 1625-49
Tower Mint 1625-42
Initial marks: lis, cross calvary,
negro's head, castle, anchor,
heart, plume, rose, harp, port-
cullis, bell, crown, tun, triangle,
star, triangle in circle

James I
Rose-ryal of
30 shillings

Charles I Unite, Tower Mint, 1625-43

	F	VF
Angels, varieties	£1750	£4000
Angels, pierced as touchpieces	£725	£1650
Unites –	£550	£1250
Double Crowns –	£400	£850
Crowns –	£200	£450

	F	VF
Halfcrowns —	£200	£400
Thistle crowns, varieties	£250	£600

Charles I Double Crown, Tower Mint with mint mark heart

Tower Mint under Parliament 1642-9 F VF
Initial marks: (P), (R), eye, sun, sceptre

	F	VF
Unites, varieties	£825	£2250
Double crowns –	£575	£1250
Crowns –	£300	£700

Briot's milled issues 1631-2
Initial marks: anemone and **B**, daisy and **B. B**

Angels	£3250	£9000
Unites	£2250	£6500
Double crowns	£1650	£4500
Crowns	£2000	£6500

Coins of provincial mints
Bristol 1645

Unites	£15000	£50000
Half unites		ext. rare

Chester 1644

Unites	£17500	£52500

Exeter 1643-44

Unites	£17500	£52500

Oxford 1642-46

Triple unites, from	£7500	£18500
Unites from	£1650	£4000
Half unites from	£1350	£3000

Truro 1642-43

Half unites		ext. rare

Shrewsbury 1644

Triple unites and unites		ext. rare

Worcester 1643-44

Unites	£18500	£60000

Charles I Oxford triple unite, 1643

HAMMERED GOLD

Siege pieces 1645-49	F	VF
Pontefract besieged 1648-49		
Unites **(F)**		ext. rare

Commonwealth 1650 gold unite

COMMONWEALTH 1649-60

	F	VF
Unites *im* sun	£1250	£3000
– *im* anchor	£3250	£9000
Double crowns *im* sun	£850	£2000
– *im* anchor	£2500	£9000
Crowns *im* sun	£650	£1500
– *im* anchor	£2000	£5000

Commonwealth crown

CHARLES II 1660-85
Hammered Coinage 1660-62

Charles II gold unite

Unites, two issues from	£1250	£3000
Double crowns –	£900	£2250
Crowns –	£950	£2500

SILVER COINS

In this section column headings are mainly F (Fine) and VF (Very Fine), but for pennies of the early Plantagenets - a series in which higher-grade coins are seldom available - prices are shown under the headings Fair and F. Again it should be noted that throughout the section prices are approximate, for the commonest types only, and are the amounts collectors can expect to pay - not dealers' buying prices. Descriptions of some early Anglo-Saxon coins are, of necessity, brief because of pressure on space. Descriptions such as 'cross/moneyer's name' indicate that a cross appears on the obverse and the moneyer's name on the reverse. For more details see Standard Catalogue of British Coins published by Spink and Son Ltd., and English Hammered Coins, Volumes 1 and 2 by J. J. North, published by Spink and Son Ltd.. (A new edition of Volume 2 was published in 1991 and a new edition of Volume 1 was published in 1994).

Anglo-Saxon Sceats and Stycas

Penny of Eadberht Praen

CUTHRED 789-807	F	VF
Non-portrait, various designs from	£625	£1600
Bust right	£675	£1750
Different moneyers, varieties etc.		
BALDRED c 825		
Bust right	£900	£3000
Cross/cross	£675	£1750
different types and moneyers		

Examples of Sceats

EARLY PERIOD c 600-750	F	VF
Silver sceats ... ...from	£50	£150

A fascinating series with great variation of styles of early art. Large numbers of types and varieties.

NORTHUMBRIAN KINGS c 737-867		
Silver sceats c 737-796 ...from	£90	£250
Copper stycas c 810-867 ...from	£20	£50

Struck for many kings. Numerous moneyers and different varieties. The copper styca is the commonest coin in the Anglo-Saxon series.

ARCHBISHOPS OF YORK c 732-900		
Silver sceats ... ...from	£75	£175
Copper stycas ... ...from	£20	£50

From here onwards until the reign of Edward I all coins are silver pennies unless otherwise stated

Kings of Kent

HEABERHT c 764	F	VF
Monogram/cross	ext. rare	
One moneyer (EOBA).		
ECGBERHT c 765-780		
Monogram/cross	£900	£2750
Two moneyers (BABBA and UDD)		
EADBERHT PRAEN 797-798		
EADBERHT REX/moneyer	£1000	£3250
Three moneyers		

Baldred penny, bust right

ANONYMOUS c 823		
Bust right	£750	£2250
Different varieties and moneyers.		

Archbishops of Canterbury

JAENBERHT 766-792	F	VF
Various types (non-portrait) from	£850	£2500
AETHELHEARD 793-805		
Various types (non-portrait) from	£800	£2250
WULFRED 805-832		
Various groups (portrait types) from	£675	£1850
CEOLNOTH 833-870		
Various groups (portrait types) from	£525	£1350

Ceolnoth penny

AETHERED 870-889
Various types (portrait, non-portrait)

	F	VF
Various types (portrait, non-portrait)	£1500	£5000

PLEGMUND 890-914
Various types (all non-portrait) from £575 £1500

Kings of Mercia

Offa portrait penny

OFFA 757-796

	F	VF
Non-portrait from	£475	£1000
Portrait from	£850	£2500

Many types and varieties

Cynethryth (wife of Offa) portrait penny

CYNETHRYTH (wife of Offa)

	F	VF
Portraits	£1750	£5500
Non-portrait	£950	£2750

COENWULF 796-821
Various types (portrait, non-portrait) from £425 £900

Coenwulf portrait penny

CEOLWULF 1821-823
Various types (portrait) £750 £2250

BEORNWULF 823-825
Various types (portrait) £750 £2250

Beornwulf penny

LUDICA 825-827
Two types (portrait) (F) £2500 £7500

WIGLAF 827-829, 830-840
Two groups (portrait, non-portrait) £1750 £5500

BERHTWULF 840-852
Two groups
(portrait, non-portrait) £825 £2750

Berhtwulf penny

BURGRED 852-874

	F	VF
One type (portrait), five variants	£185	£425

CEOLWULF II 874-c 877
Two types (portrait)) £1500 £4000

Kings of East Anglia

BEONNA c 758

	F	VF
Silver sceat	£475	£1250

AETHELBERHT LUL (died 794)
Portrait type (F) ... ... ext. rare

Eadwald penny

EADWALD c 796

	F	VF
Non-portrait types	£750	£2250

AETHELSTAN I c 850
Various types (portrait, non-portrait) £325 £850

AETHELWEARD c 850
Non-portrait types £450 £1200

EADMUND 855-870
Non-portrait types £275 £675

Viking Invaders 878-954

ALFRED

	F	VF
Imitations of Alfred pennies and halfpennies from (Many different types, portrait and non portrait)	£325	£750

ANGLIA
AETHELSTAN II 878-890
Cross/moneyer £950 £3000

OSWALD (Unknown in history except from coins)
A/cross £1200 £3750

ST EADMUND
Memorial coinage, various
legends etc. £125 £300
Many moneyers.
Halfpenny, similar £425 £1000

69

HAMMERED SILVER

St Eadmund memorial penny

	F	VF
ST MARTIN OF LINCOLN c 925		
Sword/cross	£1750	£5000
AETHELRED c 870		
Temple/cross	£1500	£4000
YORK		
SIEVERT-SIEFRED-CNUT c 897		
Crosslet/small cross	£125	£250
Many different groups and varieties		
Halfpenny, similar	£425	£900
EARL SIHTRIC (unknown)		
Non-portrait	£1750	£5000
REGNALD c 919-921		
Various types, some blundered	£1250	£4500
SIHTRIC I 921-927		
Sword/cross	£1750	£5000
ANLAF GUTHFRITHSSON 939-941		
Raven/cross	£1650	£5000
Cross/cross	£1500	£4500
Flower/cross	£1750	£5500
ANLAF SIHTRICSSON 941-944, 948-952		
Various types	£1500	£4500
SIHTRIC II c 942-943		
Shield/standard	£1650	£5000
REGNALD II c 941-943		
Cross/cross	£1650	£5000
Shield/standard	£1750	£5500
ERIC BLOODAXE 948, 952-954		
Cross/moneyer	£2250	£7500
Sword/cross	£2500	£8500

St Peter of York halfpenny

		F	VF
ST PETER OF YORK c 905-927			
Various types ... ...from	£225	£500
Halfpenny, similar	£525	£1200

Kings of Wessex

	F	VF
BEORHTRIC 786-802		
Two types (non-portrait)	ext. rare	
ECGBERHT 802-839		
FOUR GROUPS (portrait, non-portrait)	£850	£2750
Mints of Canterbury, London, Rochester, Winchester		

Aethelwulf Portrait Penny, Canterbury

	F	VF
AETHELWULF 839-858		
Four phases (portrait, non-portrait)	£375	£1000
from Mints of Canterbury, Rochester (?)		
AETHELBERHT 858-866		
Two types (portrait) ... ...from	£375	£1000
Many moneyers.		
AETHELRED I 865-871		
Portrait types ... ...from	£400	£1050
Many moneyers.		
ALFRED THE GREAT 871-899		
Portrait in style of Aethelred I ...	£450	£1250
Four other portrait types commonest being those		
with the London monogram reverse	£1050	£3000
Halfpennies	£425	£1000

Alfred the Great Penny, London monogram on reverse

	F	VF
Non-portrait types ... ...from	£375	£750
Many different styles of lettering etc.		
Halfpennies	£375	£750
EDWARD THE ELDER 899-924		
Non-portrait types:		
Cross/moneyer's name in two lines	£225	£475
Halfpennies as previous	£700	£1750

Rare penny of Edward the Elder with building on reverse

	F	VF
Portrait types:		
Bust/moneyer's name	£950	£2250
Many types, varieties and moneyers		
Types featuring buildings, floral		
designs, etc	£1250	£4000
Many types, varieties and moneyers.		

Kings of all England

AETHELSTAN 924-39 ... ...

F   VF

Aethelstan 924-939, Penny, building type reverse

Non-portrait types:

	F	VF
Cross/moneyer's name in two lines	£240	£600
Cross/cross	£275	£700

Portrait types:

bust/moneyer's name in two lines	£675	£2000
Bust/small cross	£650	£1850

Many other issues, some featuring buildings as illustrated above. There are also different mints and moneyer's names.

Aethelstan portrait penny with small cross on reverse

EADMUND 939-46

Non-portrait types:

Cross or rosette/moneyer's name in two lines	£240	£600
Silver halfpenny, similar	£675	£1500

Eadmund penny, two-line type

Portrait types:

Crowned bust/small cross	£675	£1850
Helmeted bust/cross crosslet ...	£850	£2500

Many other issues and varieties; also different mint names and moneyers.

EADRED 946-55

Non-portrait types:

Cross/moneyer's name in two lines	£225	£500
Silver halfpenny similar	£625	£1400
Rosette/moneyer's name	£275	£700

Eadred penny, portrait type

Portrait types:

	F	VF
Crowned bust/small cross	£625	£1750

Again many variations and mint names and moneyers.

HOWEL DDA (King of Wales), died c948

Small cross/moneyer's name in two lines (GILLYS)		ext. rare

EADWIG 955-59

Non-portrait types:

Cross/moneyer's name ... from	£325	£850

Many variations, some rare.

Silver halfpennies, similar	£875	£2250

Portrait types:

Bust/cross ... ... from	£2250	£7500

EADGAR 959-75

Non-portrait types:

Cross/moneyer's name ... from	£175	£400
Cross/cross ... ... from	£175	£400
Rosette/rosette ... ... from	£225	£525
Halfpennies ... ... from	£875	£2500

Eadgar, 959-957, Non Portrait Penny, Winchester

Portrait types

Pre-Reform	£700	£2000
Halfpenny, diademed bust/London monogram	£675	£1850
Reform (c.972)	£750	£2000

Many other varieties.

EDWARD THE MARTYR 975-78

Portrait types:

Bust left/small cross	£850	£2250

Many different mints and moneyers.

AETHELRED II 978-1016

Aethelred II 978-1016, Penny, Last small cross type

First small cross ... ... from	£475	£1500
First hand ... ... from	£135	£300
Second hand ... ... from	£135	£300
Benediction hand ... ... from	£675	£2000

HAMMERED SILVER

	F	VF
CRUX ... ... from	£110	£220

Aethelred II CRUX type penny

Aethelred II , Long Cross penny

	F	VF
Long Cross	£120	£240
Helmet	£125	£275
Agnus Dei	£3500	*

Other issues and varieties, many mint names and moneyers.

Aethelred II long cross penny

CNUT 1016-35
	F	VF
Quatrefoil ... ... from	£100	£200

Cnut quatrefoil type penny

	F	VF
Pointed helmet ... ... from	£90	£175

Cnut pointed helmet type penny

	F	VF
Small cross ... ... from	£80	£150
Jewel cross ... ... from	£450	£1000

Other types, and many different mint names and moneyers.

HAROLD I 1035-40
	F	VF
Jewel cross ... ... from	£275	£650

	F	VF
Long cross with trefoils ... from	£250	£600
Long cross with fleurs-de-lis from	£250	£600

Many different mint names and moneyers.

HARTHACNUT 1035-42
	F	VF
Jewel cross, bust left	£900	£2750
– bust right	£725	£2500
Arm and sceptre types	£725	£1800
Different mint names and moneyers.		
Scandinavian types struck at Lund	£225	£575

EDWARD THE CONFESSOR 1042-66
	F	VF
PACX type ... ... from	£200	£550
Radiate crown/small cross from	£100	£240
Trefoil quadrilateral	£100	£240
Small flan ... ... from	£90	£200
Expanding cross types ... from	£110	£250

Edward the Confessor Penny, Expanding Cross Type

	F	VF
Helmet types	£120	£270
Sovereign/eagles	£125	£285
Hammer cross	£100	£240

Edward the Confessor Hammer Cross Penny

	F	VF
Bust facing	£90	£200
Cross and piles	£100	£225
Large bust, facing, with sceptre	£1000	£3250

Other issues, including a unique gold penny; many different mint names and moneyers.

HAROLD II 1066
	F	VF
Crowned head left with sceptre	£600	£1350

Harold II Penny, bust left with sceptre

	F	VF
Similar but no sceptre	£625	£1450

Harold II, bust left, without sceptre

	F	VF
Crowned head right with sceptre	£1250	£4000

The Norman Kings

WILLIAM I 1066-87

		F	VF
Profile/cross fleury	... ...from	£300	£700
Bonnet ... ...from		£225	£450
Canopy ... ...from		£325	£800
Two sceptres ... ...from		£250	£625
Two stars ... ...from		£225	£450
Sword ... ...from		£325	£775

William I profile/cross fleury penny

		F	VF
Profile/cross and trefoils ...from		£375	£950
PAXS ... ...from		£200	£400

WILLIAM II 1087-1100

William II, cross voided type penny

		F	VF
Profile ... ...from		£625	£1450
Cross in quatrefoil ... ...from		£575	£1350
Cross voided ... ...from		£575	£1350
Cross pattee over fleury ...from		£600	£1450
Cross fleury and piles ... ...from		£625	£1500

Henry I penny; small bust/cross and annulets

HENRY I 1100-1135

		F	VF
Annulets ... ...from		£425	£1000
Profile/cross fleury ... ...from		£300	£800
PAX ... ...from		£275	£700
Annulets and piles ... ...from		£325	£850
Voided cross and fleurs ... ...from		£675	£1850
Pointing bust and stars ... ...from		£975	£3000
Quatrefoil and piles ... ...from		£325	£800
Profile/cross and annulets from		£1450	£4500
Cross in quatrefoil ... ...from		£650	£1600

Henry I, full face/cross fleury penny

HAMMERED SILVER

	F	VF
Full face/cross fleury	£225	£550
Double inscription	£575	£1350
Small bust/cross and annulets	£475	£1100
Star in lozenge fleury	£425	£975
Pellets in quatrefoil	£225	£500
Quadrilateral on cross fleury ...	£150	£350
Halfpennies	£1350	£3500

STEPHEN 1135-54

	F	VF
Cross moline (Watford) ...from	£225	£575

Stephen 'Watford' Penny

	F	VF
Cross moline PERERIC	£575	£1500
Voided cross and mullets	£250	£600

Stephen Penny, voided cross pattée with mullets

	F	VF
Profile/cross fleury	£400	£950
Voided cross pommée (Awbridge)	£250	£625

There are also a number of irregular issues produced during the Civil War, all of which are very rare. These include several extremely rare and attractive pieces bearing the names of Empress Matilda and barons, such as Eustace Fitzjohn and Robert de Stuteville.

The Plantagenet Kings

HENRY II 1154-89   Fair   F

Henry II Cross and Crosslets (Tealby) Penny

	Fair	F
Cross and crosslets ('Tealby' coinage)	£110	£275

The issue is classified by bust variants into six groups, struck at 32 mints.

Henry II Short Cross Penny 1b

HAMMERED SILVER

	F	VF
Short cross pennies	£55	£140

The 'short cross' coinage was introduced in 1180 and continued through successive reigns until Henry III brought about a change in 1247. HENRICVS REX appears on all these coins but they can be classified into reigns by the styles of the busts and lettering. We recommend a copy of C.R. Wren's illustrated guide The Short Cross Coinage 1180-1247, *as the best guide to identification.*

Richard I, 1189-1199, Short Cross Penny

RICHARD I 1189-99

Short cross pennies	£65	£150

JOHN 1199-1216

Short cross pennies	£55	£135

John Short Cross Penny

HENRY III 1216-72

Short cross pennies	£25	£70
Long cross pennies no sceptre	£25	£50
Long cross pennies with sceptre	£20	£50

Henry III, Long Cross Penny, no sceptre

Henry III, Long Cross Penny with sceptre

The 'long cross' pennies, first introduced in 1247, are divided into two groups: those with sceptre and those without. They also fall into five basic classes, with many varieties. We recommend C.R. Wren's, The Voided Long Cross Coinage, 1247-79 *as the best guide to identification.*

Edward I, 1st coinage, Long Cross penny

EDWARD I 1272-1307
1st coinage 1272-78

	F	VF
Long cross pennies ... ...from	£25	£75

similar in style to those of Henry III but with more realistic beard.

Edward I Penny, London

New coinage 1278-1307

Groats	£1850	£6000
Pennies, various classes, mints from	£20	£50
Halfpennies – ... ...from	£25	£75
Farthings – ... ...from	£25	£75

Edward I Farthing, London

Any new collector wishing to become serious about this area should obtain a copy of Edwardian English Silver Coins 1279-1351. Sylloge of coins of the British Isles 39 (The JJ North collection)

EDWARD II 1307-27

Pennies, various classes, mints from	£25	£60
Halfpennies ... ...from	£45	£125
Farthings ... ...from	£35	£85

EDWARD III 1327-77
1st and 2nd coinages 1327-43

Pennies (only 1st coinage) various types and mints	£185	£525
Halfpennies, different types and mints	£20	£50
Farthings	£30	£75

3rd coinage 1344-51 (Florin Coinage)

Pennies, various types and mints	£25	£75
Halfpennies –	£20	£45
Farthings	£30	£70

Edward III 1327-77, Groat Treaty Period

74

4th coinage 1351-77

	F	VF
Groats, many types and mints from	£60	£185

Edward III halfgroat Post-Treaty

		F	VF
Halfgroats –		£40	£120
Pennies –		£20	£75
Halfpennies, different types	...	£30	£80
Farthings, a few types		£85	£250

Henry IV halfpenny

RICHARD II 1377-99

	F	VF
Groats, four types from	£425	£1250

Henry VI Annulet issue halfgroat

	F	VF
Halfgroats	£275	£850
Pennies, various types, London	£175	£550
Pennies, various types, York ...	£65	£200
Pennies, Durham	£135	£425
Halfpennies, three main types ...	£30	£85
Farthings, some varieties	£100	£300

HENRY IV 1399-1413

		F	VF
Groats, varieties ... ...from		£1750	£6000
Halfgroats –		£525	£1350
Pennies –		£275	£800
Halfpennies		£200	£525
Farthings –		£650	£1750

Henry V Groat

HENRY V 1413-22

	F	VF
Groats, varieties ... ...from	£135	£450
Halfgroats	£125	£375
Pennies	£35	£100
Halfpennies	£25	£80
Farthings	£200	£575

HENRY VI 1422-61

Annulet issue 1422-1427

	F	VF
Groats	£50	£125
Halfgroats	£30	£95
Pennies	£25	£85
Halfpennies	£20	£50
Farthings	£90	£250

Rosette-Mascle issue 1427-1430

	F	VF
Groats	£50	£125
Halfgroats	£40	£100
Pennies	£35	£90
Halfpennies	£20	£55
Farthings	£125	£350

Pinecone-Mascle 1430-1434

	F	VF
Groats	£50	£120
Halfgroats	£40	£100
Pennies	£35	£100
Halfpennies	£20	£55
Farthings	£125	£350

Leaf-Mascle issue 1434-1435

	F	VF
Groats	£135	£375
Halfgroats	£100	£300
Pennies	£75	£175
Halfpennies	£30	£75

Leaf-Trefoil 1435-1438

	F	VF
Groats	£80	£225
Halfgroats	£75	£175
Pennies	£65	£165
Halfpennies	£25	£60
Farthings	£125	£350

Trefoil 1438-1443

	F	VF
Groats	£85	£250
Halfgroats	£150	£400
Halfpennies	£25	£75

Trefoil-Pellet 1443-1445

	F	VF
Groats	£150	£450

Henry VI Groat, Leaf-Pellet issue

Leaf-Pellet 1445-1454

	F	VF
Groats	£70	£200
Halfgroats	£70	£185
Pennies	£40	£110
Halfpennies	£20	£55
Farthings	£135	£375

HAMMERED SILVER

Unmarked 1445-1454	F	VF
Groats	£475	£1350
Halfgroats	£325	£850

Cross-Pellet 1454-1460

	F	VF
Groats	£120	£325
Halfgroats	£275	£650
Pennies	£50	£125
Halfpennies	£30	£80
Farthings	£200	£500

Lis-Pellet 1454-1460

Groats	£225	£750

These are many different varieties, mintmarks and mints in this reign. These prices are for commonest prices in each issue.

EDWARD IV 1st Reign 1461-1470
Heavy coinage 1461-4

	F	VF
Groats, many classes, all London	£150	£425
Halfgroats, many classes, all London	£225	£500
Pennies, different classes. London,		
York and Durham	£125	£350
Halfpennies, different classes,		
all London	£40	£100
Farthings. London	£175	£500

Edward IV Groat. Light Coinage

Light coinage 1464-70

Groats, many different issues,	F	VF
varieties, *mms* and mints from	£45	£140
Halfgroats, ditto	£40	£125
Pennies, ditto	£30	£80
Halfpennies, ditto	£25	£75
Farthings Two issues	£225	£650

Henry VI (restored), Groat, London

HENRY VI (restored) 1470-71

Groats, different mints, *mms* from	£175	£500
Halfgroats – from	£225	£550
Pennies – from	£200	£525
Halfpennies – from	£95	£250

EDWARD IV 2nd reign 1471-83	F	VF
Groats, different varieties, mints etc	£60	£160
Halfgroats	£40	£125
Pennies	£30	£90
Halfpennies	£25	£80

EDWARD IV or V 1483
mm halved sun and rose

Groats	£850	£2500
Pennies	£900	£3000
Halfpennies	£200	£625

RICHARD III 1483-85

Groat, reading EDWARD, mm boar's head on obverse, halved sun and rose on reverse	£1250	£3250
Groats, reading RICARD, London and York mints, various combinations of mms	£550	£1300
Halfgroats	£750	£1850
Pennies, York and Durham (London mint unique)	£200	£550
Halfpennies	£175	£500
Farthing	£900	£2500

PERKIN WARBECK, PRETENDER

Groat, 1494 [cf. BNJ XXVI, p. 125]	£950	£3000

The Tudor Monarchs

HENRY VII 1485-1509
Facing bust issues:

Henry VII Groat London open crown type

Groats, all London

	F	VF
Open crown without arches ...	£110	£325
Crown with two arches unjewelled	£95	£225
Crown with two jewelled arches	£70	£175
Similar but only one arch jewelled	£65	£160
Similar but tall thin lettering ...	£70	£175
Similar but single arch, tall thin lettering	£80	£225
Halfgroats, London		
Open crown without arches, tressure unbroken	£225	£650
Double arched crown	£45	£120

	F	VF
Unarched crown	£40	£100
Some varieties and different *mms*.		

Halfgroats, Canterbury

	F	VF
Open crown, without arches	£40	£110
Double arched crown	£35	£90
Some varieties and different *mms*.		

Halfgroats, York

	F	VF
Double arched crown	£40	£120
Unarched crown with tressure broken	£35	£110
Double arched crown with keys at side of bust	£35	£110
Many varieties and different mms.		

Pennies, facing bust type

	F	VF
London	£150	£425
Canterbury, open crown	£225	£500
– arched crown	£60	£150
Durham, Bishop Sherwood (S on breast)	£60	£150
York	£45	£150
Many varieties and mms.		

Pennies, 'sovereign enthroned' type

	F	VF
London, many varieties	£40	£120
Durham –	£40	£100
York –	£35	£100

Halfpennies, London

	F	VF
Open crown	£55	£125
Arched crown	£30	£80
Crown with lower arch	£25	£65
Some varieties and mms.		

Halfpennies, Canterbury

	F	VF
Open crown	£70	£175
Arched crown	£60	£125

Halfpennies, York

	F	VF
Arched crown and key below bus	£65	£135
Farthings, all London	£275	£850

Profile issues:

	F	VF
Testoons im lis, three different legends	£8000	£17500

Henry VII profile issue testoon

Groats, all London

	F	VF
Tentative issue (double band to crown)	£200	£550

Henry VII Groat, Tentative issue

	F	VF
Regular issue (triple band to crown)	£120	£375
Some varieties, and *mms*		

Halfgroats

	F	VF
London	£100	£300
– no numeral after king's name	£325	£900
Canterbury	£75	£225
York, two keys below shield	£70	£200
– XB by shield	£275	£750

HENRY VIII 1509-47
With portrait of Henry VII
1st coinage 1509-26

	F	VF
Groats, London	£125	£375
Groats, Tournai	£475	£1250
Groats, Tournai, without portrait	£1750	*
Halfgroats, London	£120	£350
Halfgroats, Canterbury, varieties	£70	£185
Halfgroats, York, varieties	£65	£175
Halfgroats, Tournai	£625	£1800
Pennies, 'sovereign enthroned' type, London	£50	£135
Pennies, Canterbury, varieties	£65	£185
Pennies, Durham, varieties	£40	£100
Halfpennies, facing bust type, London	£30	£70
Canterbury	£60	£160
Farthings, portcullis type, London	£275	£750

Henry VIII second coinage groat, with Irish title HIB REX

With young portrait of Henry VIII
2nd coinage 1526-44

	F	VF
Groats, London, varieties, *mms*	£95	£325
Groats, Irish title, HIB REX	£275	£750
Groats, York *mms*	£95	£325
Halfgroats, London *mms*	£60	£150
Halfgroats, Canterbury *mms*	£50	£135
Halfgroats, York *mms*	£50	£135
Pennies 'sovereign enthroned' type		
London, varieties, *mms*	£35	£120
Canterbury, varieties, *mms*	£65	£200
Durham –	£35	£110
York	£175	£575

Henry VIII, Halfpenny, 2nd Coingage, London

Halfpennies, facing bust type

	F	VF
London, varieties, *mms*	£25	£75
Canterbury	£35	£100
York	£65	£175
Farthings, portcullis type	£300	£700

With old bearded portrait
3rd coinage 1544-47
Posthumous issues 1547-51

	F	VF
Testoons (or shillings)		
London (Tower mint), varieties, *mms*	£700	£2400
Southwark, varieties, *mms*	£725	£2500
Bristol, varieties, *mms*	£825	£3000
Groats, six different busts, varieties, *mms*		
London (Tower mint)	£95	£350
Southwark	£95	£350
Bristol	£100	£350
Canterbury	£95	£350
London (Durham House)	£185	£500
York	£90	£325

Henry VIII third coinage groat

	F	VF
Halfgroats, only one style of bust (except York which has two), varieties, mms		
London (Tower mint)	£85	£250
Southwark	£70	£200
Bristol	£80	£250
Canterbury	£60	£175
York	£70	£200
London (Durham House)	£375	£900

Henry VIII Penny, 3rd Coinage Tower

Henry VIII Penny, 3rd Coinage, Bristol

	F	VF
Pennies (facing bust) varieties, mms		
London (Tower mint)	£40	£125
Southwark	£50	£150
London (Durham House)	£425	£900
Bristol	£60	£165
Canterbury	£45	£130
York	£45	£130
Halfpennies (facing bust) varieties, mms		
London (Tower mint)	£40	£110
Bristol	£75	£225
Canterbury	£45	£125
York	£40	£110

EDWARD VI 1547-53
1st period 1547-49

	F	VF
Shillings, London (Durham House), mm bow, patterns (?)		ext. rare
Groats, London (Tower), mm arrow	£800	£2500
Groats, London (Southwark), mm E, none	£800	£2400
Halfgroats, London (Tower), mm arrow	£450	£1000
Halfgroats, London (Southwark), mm arrow, E	£425	£1000
Halfgroats, Canterbury, mm none	£325	£850
Pennies, London (Tower), mm	£350	£1000
Pennies, London (Southwark), mm E	£375	£1100
Pennies, Bristol, mm none	£325	£900
Halfpennies, London (Tower), mm uncertain	£350	£950
Halfpennies, Bristol, mm none	£325	£850

Edward VI 2nd period shilling. Tower mint with mintmark Y.

Edward VI, Shilling, 2nd period Canterbury with mintmark t.

2nd period 1549-50

	F	VF
Shillings, London (Tower) various mms	£135	£525
Shillings, Bristol, mm TC	£750	£2250
Shillings, Canterbury, mm T or t	£165	£600
Shillings, London (Durham House), mm bow, varieties	£150	£550

3rd period £550-53

	F	VF
Base silver (similar to issues of 2nd period)		
Shillings, London (Tower), mm lis, lion, rose	£150	£525
Pennies, London (Tower), mm escallop	£65	£180
Pennies, York, mm mullet	£60	£175
Halfpennies, London (Tower)	£175	£500

Fine Silver	F	VF
Crown 1551 mm Y, 1551-53	£700	£1800
mm tun		

Edward VI Halfcrown 1551, walking horse

	F	VF
Halfcrown, walking horse, 1551, mm Y	£650	£1500
Halfcrowns, galloping horse, 1551-52, mm tun	£650	£1600

Edward VI 1552 halfcrown galloping horse

	F	VF
Halfcrowns, walking horse, 1553, mm tun	£975	£3500
Shillings, mm Y, tun	£110	£375
Sixpences, London (Tower), mm y, tun	£125	£525
Sixpences, York, mm mullet ...	£175	£650
Threepences, London (Tower), mm tun	£175	£675
Threepences, York mm mullet ...	£375	£1100
Pennies, sovereign type	£975	£3500
Farthings, portcullis type	£1250	*

Mary Groat

Mary Portrait Penny

MARY 1553-54

	F	VF
Groats, mm pomegranate	£120	£375
Halfgroats, similar	£675	£2000
Pennies, rev VERITAS TEMP FILIA ...	£575	£1850
Pennies, rev CIVITAS LONDON	£575	£1850

PHILIP AND MARY 1554-58

	F	VF
Shillings, full titles, without date	£350	£1200
– also without XII	£375	£1350
– dated 1554	£350	£1200
– dated 1554, English titles ...	£375	£1350
– dated 1555, English titles only	£350	£1250
– dated 1554, English titles only also without XII	£425	£1500
– 1555, as last	£650	*
– 1554 but date below bust ...	£1650	*
– 1555 but date below bust ...	£1650	*
– 1555 similar to previous but without ANG	£2000	*
Sixpences, full titles, 1554	£350	£1200
– full titles, undated		ext rare
– English titles, 1555	£350	£1350
– similar but date below bust, 1554	£675	*
– English titles, 1557	£350	£1250
– similar, but date below bust, 1557	£1000	*
Groats, mm lis	£125	£400
Halfgroats, mm lis	£375	£1200

Philip and Mary Shilling, 1554 and full titles

	F	VF
Pennies, mm lis	£400	£1350
Base pennies, without portrait ...	£75	£225

HAMMERED SILVER

ELIZABETH I 1558-1603	F	VF
Hammered coinage, 1st issue 1558-61		
Shillings ELIZABETH		
Wire-line circles	£425	£1600
Beaded inner circles	£175	£700
ET for Z	£100	£350

Edward VI shilling greyhound countermark (reign of Elizabeth), and Elizabeth I hammered groat

Groats		
Wire-line inner circles	£135	£550
Beaded inner circles	£75	£250
ET for Z	£60	£200
Halfgroats		
Wire-line inner circles	£135	£500
Beaded inner circles	£45	£135

Elizabeth I Penny, wire-line inner circle

Pennies		
Wire-line inner circles	£200	£700
Beaded inner circles	£30	£80
Countermarked shillings of Edward VI, 1560-61		
With portcullis mark (Current for 4½d) **(F)**	£2000	*
With greyhound mark (current for 2½d) **(F)**	£2500	*

Hammered coinage, 2nd issue 1561-82		
Sixpences, dated 1561-82	£60	£180
Threepences, 1561-82	£40	£125
Halfgroats, undated	£50	£165
Threehalfpences, 1561-62, 1564-70,		
1572-79, 1581-82	£40	£110
Pennies, undated	£25	£90
Threefarthings, 1561-62, 1568,		
1572-78, 1581-82	£75	£185

Elizabeth I Halfcrown, 1601

Hammered coinage, 3rd issue 1583-1603		
Crowns, im **1**	£1350	£3000
Crowns, im **2**	£1750	£5000
Halfcrowns, im **1**	£850	£2000
Halfcrowns, im **2 (F)**	£2000	£6000
Shillings ELIZAB	£100	£350
Sixpences, 1582-1602	£55	£175
Halfgroats, E D G ROSA etc	£25	£70
Pennies	£25	£70
Halfpennies, portcullis type ...	£25	£75

There are many different mintmarks, such as lis, bell, lion etc., featured on the hammered coins of Elizabeth I, and these marks enable one to date those coins which are not themselves dated. For more details see J.J. North's English Hammered Coinage, Volume 2.

Elizabeth I Miled Coinage, Sixpence, 1562

Milled Coinage		
Shillings		
large size	£350	£1000
Intermediate	£250	£650
Small	£225	£550
Sixpences		
1561	£100	£350
1562	£90	£325
1563-64, 1566	£90	£325
1567-68	£85	£300
1570-71	£275	£900
Groats, undated	£150	£500
Threepences, 1561, 1562-64 ...	£110	£350
Halfgroats	£175	£550
Threefarthings	ext.rare	*

The Stuart Kings

JAMES I 1603-25	F	VF
1st coinage 1603-04		
Crowns, rev EXURGAT etc	£1050	£3000
Halfcrowns –	£1200	£3500
Shillings, varieties	£85	£300
Sixpences, dated 1603-04,		
varieties	£60	£200
Halfgroats, undated	£30	£85
Pennies –	£25	£70

James I halfcrown with plume over shield on reverse

	F	VF
Shillings	£90	£300
– Plume over reverse shield ...	£200	£675
Sixpences dated 1621-24	£65	£200
Halfgroats	£20	£50
Pennies	£20	£50
Halfpennies	£15	£35

James I Sixpence, 1603

2nd coinage 1604-19		
Crowns rev QVAE DEVS etc ...	£850	£2750
Halfcrowns –	£1100	£3250

James I sixpence of 1622

CHARLES I 1625-1649
Tower Mint 1625-1643
Crowns
(Obv. King on horseback. Rev. shield)

James I 2nd coinage shilling

Shillings, varieties	£75	£250
Sixpences, dated 1604-15,		
varieties etc.	£50	£175
Halfgroats, varieties	£20	£50
Pennies	£20	£50
Halfpennies	£15	£45

1st horseman/square shield		
im lis, cross calvary	£750	£1850
As last/plume above shield		
im lis, cross calvary, castle ...	£1000	£3000
2nd horseman/oval shield		
im plume, rose harp.		
Some varieties, from	£650	£1650
3rd horseman/round shield		
im bell, crown, tun, anchor,		
triangle, star, portcullis, triangle		
in circle. Some varieties, from	£650	£16\50

Halfcrowns
(Obv. King on horseback. Rev. shield)

James I Shilling, 3rd Coinage

3rd coinage 1619-25		
Crowns	£650	£1650
– Plume over reverse shield ...	£800	£2000
Halfcrowns	£225	£700
– Plume over reverse shield ...	£375	£1100

*Charles I
Tower halfcrown:
first horseman*

HAMMERED SILVER

	F	VF
1st horseman/square shield		
im lis, cross calvary, negro's head, castle, anchor.		
Many varieties, from	£200	£650
2nd horseman/oval shield		
im plume, rose, harp, portcullis.		
Many varieties, from	£110	£350
3rd horseman/round shield		
im bell, crown, tun, portcullis, anchor, triangle, star		
Many varieties, from	£75	£200
4th horseman/round shield		
im star, triangle in circle	£60	£150

*Charles I
Tower Halfcrown,
mintmark
triangle*

Shillings

	F	VF
1st bust/square shield		
***im* lis, cross calvary**		
Some varieties	£110	£400
2nd bust/square shield		
im cross calvary, negro's head, castle, anchor, heart, plume		
Many varieties, from	£90	£375
3rd bust/oval shield		
im plume, rose	£65	£225
4th bust/oval or round shield		
im harp, portcullis, bell, crown, tun		
Many varieties, from	£50	£175
5th bust/square shield		
im tun, anchor, triangle		
Many varieties, from	£50	£175
6th bust/square shield		
im anchor, triangle, star, triangle in circle		
Some varieties, from	£40	£150

Sixpences
(early ones are dated)

	F	VF
1st bust/square shield, date above		
1625 *im* lis, cross calvary		
1626 *im* cross calvary	£90	£350
2nd bust/square shield, date above		
1625, 1626 *im* cross calvary		
1626, 1627 *im* negro's head		
1626, 1628 *im* castle		
1628, 1629 *im* anchor		
1629 *im* heart		
1630 *im* heart, plume	£100	£400

	F	VF
3rd bust/oval shield		
im plume, rose	£70	£250
4th bust/oval or round shield		
im harp, portcullis, bell, crown, tun	£45	£150

Charles I Tower sixpence mm bell

	F	VF
5th bust/square shield		
im tun, anchor, triangle		
Many varieties, from	£60	£200
6th bust/square shield		
im triangle, star	£50	£200
Halfgroats		
Crowned rose both sides		
im lis, cross calvary, blackamoor's head	£25	£80
2nd bust/oval shield		
im plume, rose	£25	£80
3rd bust/oval shield		
im rose, plume	£30	£90
4th bust/oval or round shield,		
im harp, crown, portcullis, bell, tun, anchor, triangle, star		
Many varieties from	£20	£50
5th bust/round shield		
im anchor	£30	£90
Pennies		
Uncrowned rose both sides		
im one or two pellets, lis, negro's head	£20	£50
2nd bust/oval shield		
im plume	£25	£75
3rd bust/oval shield		
im plume, rose	£20	£50
4th bust/oval shield		
im harp, one or two pellets, portcullis, bell, triangle	£15	£45
5th bust/oval shield		
im one or two pellets, none	£15	£45
Halfpennies		
Uncrowned rose both sides		
im none	£15	£40

Tower Mint, under Parliament 1643-48

	F	VF
Crowns		
(Obv. King on horseback, Rev. shield)		
4th horseman/round shield		
im (**P**), (**R**), eye sun	£800	£2000
5th horseman/round shield		
im sun, sceptre	£850	£2250
Halfcrowns		
(Obv. King on horseback, Rev. shield)		
3rd horseman/round shield		
im (**P**), (**R**), eye sun	£50	£200
im (**P**), foreshortened horse	£150	£475
5th horseman (tall)/round shield		
im sun, sceptre	£75	£225

F   VF

Sixpence of Broit's 2nd milled issue

Charles I Parliament shilling, mm eye

Briot's hammered issues 1638-39	F	VF
im: anchor, triangle over anchor		
Halfcrowns	£750	£1850
Shillings	£350	£850

Shillings (revs. all square shield)
6th bust (crude)

im (**P**), (**R**), eye, sun	£45	£165
7th bust (tall, slim)		
im sun, sceptre	£60	£225
8th bust (shorter, older)		
im sceptre	£65	£250

Sixpences (revs. all square shield)
6th bust

im (**P**), (**R**), eye sun	£75	£225
7th bust		
im (**R**), eye, sun, sceptre ...	£65	£200
8th bust, (crude style)		
im eye, sun	£110	£375

Halfgroats
4th bust/round shield

im (**P**), (**R**), eye sceptre ...	£20	£70
7th bust (old/round shield)		
im eye, sun, sceptre	£20	£70

Pennies
7th bust/oval shield

im one or two pellets	£25	£75

*Charles I
Crown
of Exeter*

PROVINCIAL MINTS
York 1642-44
im: lion

Halfcrowns, varieties from	£275	£800
Shillings –	£250	£650
Sixpences –	£275	£700
Threepences	£70	£175

Aberystwyth 1638-42
im: open book

Halfcrowns, varieties from	£850	£3250
Shillings –	£400	£1200
Sixpences –	£325	£850
Groats –	£60	£175

Charles I Briot's crown

Briot's 1st milled issued 1631-32
im: flower and **B**

Crowns	£800	£2000
Halfcrowns	£450	£1350
Shillings	£325	£700
Sixpences	£165	£400
Halfgroats	£65	£135
Pennies	£70	£180

Briot's 2nd milled issue 1638-39
im: anchor, anchor and B, anchor and mullet

Halfcrowns	£275	£800
Shillings	£150	£425
Sixpences	£90	£250

Aberystwyth groat

Threepences –	£50	£135
Halfgroats –	£55	£150
Pennies –	£70	£200
Halfpennies	£175	£500

Aberystwyth – Furnace 1647-48
im: crown

Halfcrowns from	£1850	£5000
Shillings	£2500	*

HAMMERED SILVER

	F	VF
Sixpences	£1250	£2750
Groats	£250	£575
Threepences	£225	£500
Halfgroats	£300	£800
Pennies	£725	£2000

Shrewsbury 1642
mm: plume without band

	F	VF
Pounds, varieties from	£2250	£5000
Halfpounds –	£950	£2250
Crowns –	£950	£2400
Halfcrowns –	£550	£1500
Shillings –	£900	£2750

Oxford 1642-46
mm: plume with band

	F	VF
Pounds, varieties from	£2250	£5250
Halfpounds –	£1000	£2350
Crowns –	£850	£2250
Halfcrowns –	£275	£750
Shillings –	£300	£850
Sixpences –	£250	£750
Groats –	£150	£400
Threepences –	£110	£250
Halfgroats –	£110	£300
Pennies –	£185	£500

Bristol 1643-45
im: Bristol monogram, acorn, plumelet

	F	VF
Halfcrowns, varieties from	£350	£900

Charles I halfcrown of York with mm lion

	F	VF
Shillings –	£300	£850
Sixpences –	£250	£700
Groats –	£175	£450
Threepences –	£175	£475
Halfgroats –	£275	£650
Pennies –	£425	£950

Charles I sixpence, Bristol 1644

A, B, and plumes issues
Associated with Thomas Bushell; previously assigned to Lundy

	F	VF
Halfcrowns, varieties from	£900	£2750

	F	VF
Shillings –	£425	£1250
Sixpences –	£240	£600
Groats –	£200	£500
Threepences –	£200	£450
Halfgroats –	£475	£1000

Truro 1642-43
im: rose, bugle

	F	VF
Crowns, varieties	£375	£900
Halfcrowns –	£900	£2500
Shillings –	£3000	*

Bristol shilling 1644

Exeter 1643-46
im Ex, rose, castle

	F	VF
Halfpounds		ext. rare
Crowns, varieties	£425	£900
Halfcrowns	£325	£800
Shillings	£375	£900
Sixpences	£325	£750
Groats	£135	£300
Threepences	£135	£300
Halfgroats –	£250	£650
Pennies	£350	£950

Worcester 1643-4
im: castle, helmet, leopard's head, lion, two lions, lis, rose, star

	F	VF
Halfcrowns, many varieties	£750	£2050

Salopia (Shrewsbury) 1644
im: helmet, lis, rose (in legend)

	F	VF
Halfcrowns, many varieties	£850	£2750

Worcester or Salopia (Shrewsbury)
im: bird, boar's head, lis, castle, cross, and annulets, helmet, lion, lis, pear, rose, scroll

	F	VF
Shillings, varieties	£1000	£3500
Sixpences	£900	£3000
Groats	£600	£1500
Threepences	£350	£750
Halfgroats	£525	£1250

'HC' mint (probably Hartlebury Castle, Worcester 1646)
im: pear, three pears

	F	VF
Halfcrowns	£1500	£4000

Chester 1644
im: cinquefoil, plume, prostrate gerb, three gerbs

	F	VF
Halfcrowns, varieties	£750	£2500
Shillings	£1350	*
Threepences	£850	£2000

Welsh Marches mint? 1644

	F	VF
Halfcrowns...	£900	£2500

Welsh Marches mint, halfcrown

SIEGE PIECES
Carlisle besieged 1644-45

	F	VF
Three shillings	£6500	£15000
Shillings (**F**)	£4500	£10000

Newark besieged many times
(surrendered May 6, 1646)

	F	VF
Halfcrowns, 1645-46 (**F**)	£750	£1500

Newark Besieged, Shilling, dated 1645

	F	VF
Shillings, 1645-46, varieties (**F**)	£600	£1250
Ninepences, 1645-46	£550	£1100
Sixpences	£650	£1350

Pontefract besieged 1648-49

	F	VF
Two shillings, 1648	£5250	£15000
Shillings, 1648, varieties	£1650	£4000

Ponefract Besieged 1648, Siege Shilling

Scarborough besieged 1644-45
Many odd values issued here, all of which are extremely rare. The coin's value was decided by the intrinsic value of the piece of metal from which it was made.

HAMMERED SILVER

	F	VF

Examples: 5s 8d, 2s 4d, 1s 9d, 1s 3d, 7d etc. (**F**). Collectors could expect to pay at least **£6500** or more in F and **£15000** in VF for any of these.

COMMONWEALTH 1649-60

	F	VF
Crowns, *im* sun 1649,51-54, 56 ...	£750	£1650
Halfcrowns, *im* sun 1649, 1651-6	£250	£600
—*im* anchor 1658-60	£850	£2250

Commonwealth Shilling, 1651

	F	VF
Shillings, *im* sun 1649, 1661-87	£150	£350
—*im* anchor 1658-60	£575	£1350

A superb 1651 sixpence

	F	VF
Sixpences, *im* sun 1649, 1651-7	£125	£325
—*im* anchor 1658-6	£525	£1250
Halfgroats undated	£30	£90
Pennies undated	£25	£70
Halfpennies undated	£25	£70

CHARLES II 1660-85
Hammered coinage 1660-62

		F	VF
Halfcrowns, three issues ...	from	£250	£675
Shillings—	from	£150	£475

Charles II hammered issue shilling

		F	VF
Sixpences—		£135	£400
Fourpences, third issue only ...		£30	£80
Threepences—	from	£30	£70
Twopences, three issues	from	£25	£65
Pennies—	from	£25	£65

'ROYAL' AND 'ROSE' BASE METAL FARTHINGS

Until 1613 English coins were struck only in gold or silver — the monarchy considered that base metal issues would be discreditable to the royal prerogative of coining. However, silver coins had become far too small, farthings so tiny that they had to be discontinued. So to meet demands for small change James I authorised Lord Harington to issue copper farthing tokens. Subsequently this authority passed in turn to the Duke of Lennox, the Duchess of Richmond and Lord Maltravers. It ceased by order of Parliament in 1644.

JAMES I
Royal farthing tokens

	Fair	F	VF	EF
Type 1 Harington (circa 1613). Small copper flan with tin-washed surface, mint-mark between sceptres below crown	£10	£30	£75	£150
Type 2 Harington (circa 1613). Larger flan, no tin wash	£15	£15	£40	£90
Type 3 Lennox (1614-25). IACO starts at 1 o'clock position	£3	£10	£25	£75
Type 4 Lennox (1622-25). Oval flan, IACO starts at 7 o'clock	£8	£25	£65	£140

CHARLES I
Royal farthing tokens

Type 1 Richmond (1625-34). Single arched crown	£2	£8	£25	£65
Type 2 Transitional (circa 1634). Double arched crown	£6	£20	£50	£125
Type 3 Maltravers (1634-36). Inner circles	£3	£10	£30	£75
Type 4 Richmond (1625-34). As Type 1 but oval	£8	£25	£60	£140
Type 5 Maltravers (1634-36). Double arched crown	£10	£30	£70	£120

Rose farthing tokens (rose on reverse)

Type 1 Small thick flan	£3	£10	£30	£80
Type 2 Same, but single arched crown	£2	£7	£25	£75
Type 3 Same, but sceptres below crown	£10	£25	£50	£90

James I Harington farthings, types 1, 2 and 3 (left to right)

Charles I Richmond, Maltravers and Rose farthings (left to right)

MILLED COINAGE from 1656

Again it must be stressed that the prices shown in this guide are the approximate amounts collectors can expect to pay for coins — they are not dealers' buying prices. Information for this guide is drawn from auction results and dealers' lists, with the aim of determining firm valuations. Prices still vary enormously from sale to sale and from one dealer's list to another. Allowance must also be made for the variance in the standards of grading. The prices given here aim at a reasonable assessment of the market at the time of compilation, but they are not the product of computers, which would, in any case, provide only average (not necessarily accurate) prices. It is not possible to forecast such values because of the erratic fluctuations that can occur, not only in boom conditions but also during times of economic uncertainty, and an annual catalogue of this type cannot be up to date on the bullion prices of common sovereigns, for example. If you are buying or selling bullion gold coins, refer to current quotations from bullion dealers.

With some denominations in the silver and copper series, column headings indicating condition change at the beginning of the lists of George III coins. The condition (grade) of a coin is of great importance in determining its market value. Notes on grading and on abbreviations etc. used in these price guides appear elsewhere in this publication.

Cromwell gold patterns

These were struck by order of Cromwell, with the consent of the Council. The dies were made by Thomas Simon, and the coins were struck on Peter Blondeau's machine. The fifty shillings and the broad were struck from the same dies, but the fifty shillings has the edge inscription PROTECTOR LITERIS LITERAE NUMMIS CORONA ER SALUS, while the broad is not so thick and has a grained edge. No original strikings of the half broad are known, but some were struck from dies made by John Tanner in 1738. All three denominations are dated 1656.

Oliver Cromwell gold half broad 1656

	F	VF	EF	Unc
Fifty shillings	*	£25000	£45000	*
Broad	*	£4750	£11000	£16000
Half broad	*	£4500	£8000	*

Five guineas

	F	VF	EF	Unc
CHARLES II				
1668-78 pointed end to trnctn of bust	£1750	£3250	£9000	*
1668, 69, 75—eleph below bust	£1750	£3250	£9000	£17500
1675-8—eleph & castle below bust	£1750	£3250	£9000	*
1678-84 rounded end to trnctn	£1750	£3000	£8000	*
1680-4—eleph & castle	£1875	£3500	£9000	*
JAMES II				
1686 sceptres in wrong order on rev	£2000	£3750	£10000	*
1687-8 sceptres correct	£2000	£3750	£10000	*
1687-8 eleph & castle	£2000	£4000	£10000	*
WILLIAM AND MARY				
1691-4 no prov mark	£1900	£3500	£8500	*
1691-4 eleph & castle	£2000	£3750	£9000	*
WILLIAM III				
1699-1700 no prov mark	£1750	£2750	£8500	*
1699 eleph & castle	£1850	£3250	£9000	*
1701 new bust 'fine work'	£2000	£2750	£8000	£9000

Charles II 1676 five guineas, elephant and castle

FIVE GUINEAS

George II 1729 five guineas

	F	VF	EF	Unc
ANNE				
Pre-Union with Scotland				
1703 VIGO below bust	*	*	£125000	*
1705-6 plain below	£2000	£3750	£12000	*
Post-Union with Scotland				
1706	£1750	£3000	£9500	£17500
1709 Larger lettering, wider shield and crowns	£1750	£3250	£9500	*
1711, 1713-4 broader bust	£1750	£3000	£9500	*

Pre-Union reverses have separate shields (top and right) for England and Scotland. Post-Union reverses have the English and Scottish arms side by side on the top and bottom shields.

	F	VF	EF	Unc
GEORGE I				
1716, 17, 20, 26	£2250	£3500	£14000	*
GEORGE II				
1729, 31, 35, 38, 41 YH	£1700	£2250	£5750	£7500
1729 E,I,C, below head	£1700	£2500	£6250	£8000
1746 OH, lima below	£1700	£2750	£6250	£8500
1748, 53 plain below	£1700	£2750	£6250	£8500
GEORGE III				
1770, 73, 77 patterns only	*	*	£45000	£70000

Two guineas

Charles II 1664 two guineas elephant below bust

	F	VF	EF	Unc
CHARLES II				
1664, 5, 9, 71 pointed end to trnctn	£875	£1850	£6500	*
1664 elephant below	£875	£1850	£6500	*
1675-84 rounded end to trnctn	£800	£1750	£5000	£9500
1676, 78, 82-84 eleph & castle below bust	£900	£2000	£6750	*
1678 elephant below				ext. rare
JAMES II				
1687	£1200	£3000	£8000	*
1688/9	£1350	£3250	£9000	*
WILLIAM AND MARY				
1691, 3, 4 eleph & castle	£1100	£1850	£6500	*
1693, 4 no prov mark	£1100	£2000	£5750	£7500
WILLIAM III				
1701	£1100	£3000	£5000	*
ANNE				
(none struck before Union)				
1709, 11, 13, 14	£900	£2000	£4000	£7000
GEORGE I				
1717,20,26	£900	£1650	£3750	£5250
GEORGE II				
1734, 5, 8, 9,YH (F)	£575	£850	£2500	£4000
1739, 40 intermediate head (F)	£600	£950	£2750	£4500
1748, 53 OH	£625	£1000	£2850	£4000
GEORGE III				
1768, 73, 77 patterns only	*	*	£14000	£20000

James II 1687 two guineas

Guineas

	F	VF	EF	Unc
CHARLES II				
1663 pointed trnctn	£625	£2250	£6250	*
1663—eleph	£625	£2250	£6250	*
1664 trnctn indented	£625	£2250	£6000	*
1664—eleph	*	*ext. rare		*

Charles II 1663 guinea elephant below bust

Anne 1713 guinea

George III 1768 guinea

	F	VF	EF	Unc
1664-73 sloping pointed trnctn	£650	£1850	£4750	*
1664, 5, 8 — eleph	£800	£2350	£5250	*
1672-84 rounded trnctn	£525	£1650	£4000	*
1674-84 — eleph & castle	£750	£2000	£6000	*
1677, 8 — eleph			ext. rare	

JAMES II

	F	VF	EF	Unc
1685, 6 1st bust	£525	£1500	£3500	£6000
1685 — eleph & castle	£600	£1500	£4000	*
1686-8 2nd bust	£600	£1500	£3500	£6000
1686-8 — eleph & castle	£600	£1500	£4000	*

WILLIAM AND MARY

	F	VF	EF	Unc
1689-94 no prov mark	£500	£1850	£4250	£6000
1689-94 eleph & castle	£525	£2000	£4500	*
1692 eleph	£700	£2500	£5250	*

WILLIAM III

	F	VF	EF	Unc
1695, 6 1st bust	£400	£850	£3500	£4000
1695, 7 — eleph & castle	*	*	*	*
1697-1701 2nd bust	£350	£850	£3500	*
1698-1701 — eleph & castle	£800	£2750	*	*
1701 3rd bust 'fine work'	£500	£1500	£4250	*

ANNE
Pre-Union[1]

	F	VF	EF	Unc
1702, 1705-7 plain below bust	£600	£1000	£3500	£5250
1703 VIGO below	£3750	£8000	£22500	*

Post Union[1]

	F	VF	EF	Unc
1707, 8 1st bust	£425	£900	£1650	£2950
1707 — eleph & castle	£650	£1750	£4250	*
1707-9 2nd bust	£425	£850	£1850	£3000
1708-9 — eleph & castle	£700	£2000	£4000	*
1710-1714 3rd bust	£425	£750	£1850	£2850

[1]See note in prices of five guinea pieces for Anne.

GEORGE I

	F	VF	EF	Unc
1714 1st head PR. EL. (Prince Elector) in rev legend	*	£2000	£3500	£5000
1715 2nd head, tie with two ends	£350	£900	£2750	£3000
1715 3rd head, hair not curling round trnctn	£300	£850	£2750	£2850
1716-23 4th head, tie with loop	£300	£850	£2750	£2850
1721, 2 — eleph & castle	*		ext. rare	
1723-7 5th head, smaller, older bust	£300	£850	£2750	£2850
1726 — eleph & castle	£1000	£3000	*	*

GEORGE II

	F	VF	EF	Unc
1727 1st YH, small lettering	£750	£1750	£3750	£5000
1727, 8 — larger lettering	£525	£1350	£3250	*
1729-32 2nd YH (narrower)	£475	£1200	£2750	*
1729, 31, 2 — E.I.C. below	£550	£1750	£3650	£4500
1732-8 — larger lettering	£425	£900	£2500	£5000
1732 — — E.I.C. below	£500	£1400	£3650	*
1739, 40, 43 intermediate head	£250	£750	£2000	£3000
1739 — E.I.C. below	£500	£1100	£3500	*
1745, 6 — larger lettering	£325	£850	£2500	*
1745 — LIMA below	£1200	£3800	£6250	*
1747-53, 5, 6, 8, 9, 60, OH	£300	£600	£1500	£2500

GEORGE III

	F	VF	EF	Unc
1761, 1st head	£750	£2000	£3500	£4500
1763, 4, 2nd head	£500	£1500	£3500	*
1765-73, 3rd head	£250	£400	£1000	£1500
1774-9, 81-6, 4th head	£200	£325	£700	£900
1789-99, 5th head, 'spade' rev (F)	£200	£300	£550	£750
1813, 6th head, rev shield in Garter ('Military guinea')	£475	£925	£1650	£2500

William and Mary 1691 half guinea

William III 1695 half guinea

George I 1719 half guinea

George I half guinea, 1725

George II 1756 half guinea

George III 1788 half guinea with 'spade' type shield on reverse

George I 1718 quarter guinea

Half Guineas

	F	VF	EF	Unc
CHARLES II				
1669-72 bust with pointed trnctn	£500	£925	£3250	*
1672-84 rounded trnctn...	£500	£925	£3500	*
1676-8, 80, 82-4 — eleph & castle	£550	£1200	£4000	*
JAMES II				
1686-8 no prov mark	£425	£950	£3000	*
1686 eleph & castle	£1250	*	*	*
WILLIAM AND MARY				
1689 1st busts	£500	£1650	£3500	*
1690-4 2nd busts	£600	£1750	£3750	*
1691-2 — eleph & castle	£650	£1275	£4000	*
1692 — eleph				ext. rare
WILLIAM III				
1695 no prov mark	£300	£625	£2250	£3000
1695, 6 eleph & castle	£425	£850	£2650	*
1697-1701 larger harp on rev	£300	£600	£2250	*
1698 — eleph & castle	£350	£875	£3000	*
ANNE				
Pre-Union[1]				
1702, 5 plain below bust	£525	£1650	£4000	*
1703 VIGO below	£3250	£8500	£17500	*
Post-Union[1]				
1707-14 plain	£250	£700	£2000	£2850
[1]See note in prices of five guineas for Anne.				
GEORGE I				
1715, 17-24, 1st head	£300	£575	£1350	£2500
1721 eleph & castle	*	*	*	*
1725-7, smaller older head	£250	£425	£1000	£2000
GEORGE II				
1728-39 YH	£325	£650	£2000	*
1729-32, 9 — E.I.C. below	£450	£1200	£2750	*
1740, 3, 5, 6, intermediate head	£375	£900	£2500	*
1745 — LIMA below	£1250	£2500	£4750	*
1747-53, 5, 6, 58-60 OH	£250	£425	£1250	£1750
GEORGE III				
1762, 3, 1st head	£400	£1000	£2500	*
1764-6, 8, 9, 72-5, 2nd head	£200	£400	£850	£1250
1774, 5, 3rd head	£600	£1500	£2750	*
1775-9, 81, 83-6, 4th head	£110	£200	£400	£875
1787-91, 93-8, 1800, 5th head	£100	£175	£350	£525
1801-3, 6th head	£90	£135	£275	£525
1804, 6, 8-11, 13, 7th head	£80	£135	£250	£475

Third guineas

	F	VF	EF	Unc
GEORGE III				
1797-1800 1st head	£60	£85	£200	£300
1801-3 — date close to crown on reverse	£60	£85	£200	£300
1804, 6, 8-11, 2nd head	£60	£80	£200	£300

Quarter guineas

	F	VF	EF	Unc
GEORGE I				
1718	£80	£165	£350	£500
GEORGE III				
1762	£80	£165	£350	£500

Britannias

(See under Decimal Coinage)

Five pounds

GEORGE III	F	VF	EF	Unc
1820 pattern (F)	*	*	*	£65000
GEORGE IV				
1826 proof	*	*	£7000	£10000
VICTORIA				
1839 proof with 'Una and the Lion' rev (F)	*	*	£16000	£25000
1887 JH (F) £425		£500	£750	£1000
1887 proof	*	*	£1450	£2750
1887 proof no B.P.	*	*	£1500	£3000
1893 OH (F) £475		£650	£1000	£1900
1893 proof	*	*	£1500	£3250
EDWARD VII				
1902 (F) £400		£500	£700	£950
1902 proof	*	*	£700	£950
GEORGE V				
1911 proof (F) ...	*	*	£950	£1500
GEORGE VI				
1937 proof	*	*	*	£725

ELIZABETH II
In 1984 the Royal Mint issued the first of an annual issue of Brilliant Uncirculated £5 coins. These bear the symbol 'U' in a circle to the left of the date on the reverse to indicate the standard of striking.

1981 proof...	£425
1984	£425
1985	£450
1986	£450
1987 new effigy	£450
1988	£450
1989 500th anniversary of the sovereign, BU ...	£500
1990 Queen Mother's 90th birthday, proof	£625
1990	£475
1991	£500
1992	£500
1993 Coronation, proof	£750
1993	£525
1994	£550
1995	£575
1996 Queen's 70th Birthday, proof	£675
... ... BU	£600
1997 Golden Wedding, proof	£700
1997	£580
1998 Prince Charles 50th Birthday, proof...	£600
1998 New Portrait	£535
1999 Diana Memorial, proof	£600
1999 Millennium, proof	£600
1999	£450
2000 Millennium, proof	£525
2000 Queen Mother Centenary, proof	£525
2000	£475
2001 Victorian Anniversary, proof	£550
2001 as above, reverse frosting, proof	£750
2001	£450
2002 Golden Jubilee, proof	£600
2002 Shield reverse, proof	£600
2002 Queen Mother memorial	£600
2003 Coronation Jubilee, proof	£560
2004 Entente Cordial, proof	£560
2005 Queens 80th Birthday, proof	£745

Two pounds

GEORGE III	F	VF	EF	Unc
1820 pattern (F)	*	*	£7500	£13500

George III 1820 pattern two pounds

GEORGE IV ...	F	VF	EF	Unc
1823 St George on reverse(F)£375		£500	£900	£2000
1826 proof, shield reverse	*	*	£2500	£4500

William IV 1831 proof two pounds

WILLIAM IV				
1831 proof	*	*	£3750	£6000
VICTORIA				
1887 JH (F) ... £185		£220	£350	£450
1887 proof	*	*	£650	£1000
1893 OH (F) ... £220		£300	£450	£725
1893 proof	*	*	£750	£1000
EDWARD VII				
1902 (F) £175		£225	£350	£425
1902 proof	*	*	£325	£425
GEORGE V				
1911 proof (F)	*	*	*	£625

1937 proof two pounds

GEORGE VI				
1937 proof ...	*	*	*	£425

TWO POUNDS

ELIZABETH II	F	VF	EF	Unc
1983 proof...				£225
1986 Commonwealth Games, proof				£225
1987 proof...				£250
1988 proof...				£250
1989 500th anniversary of the sovereign, proof				£275
1990 proof...				£250
1991 proof...				£250
1993 proof...				£250
1994 gold proof				£425
1994 gold proof 'mule'				£750
1995 VE day gold proof				£375
1995 50th Anniversary of UN, proof				£300
1996 European Football Championship				£350
1997 Bimetal gold proof...				£350
1998 New portrait, proof				£300
1999 Rugby World Cup				£300
2000 proof...				£275
2001 Marconi, proof				£295
2002 Shield reverse, proof				£300
2003 DNA bi-colour proof				£295
2004 Locomotive proof				£325
2005 2nd W.War proof				£325

Sovereigns

GEORGE III	F	VF	EF	Unc
1817 (F)	£200	£325	£925	£1500
1818	£225	£475	£1100	£1850
1819	£12500	£25000	£55000	*
1820	£200	£350	£1100	£1650

GEORGE III
Type Laureate head/St George

	F	VF	EF	Unc
1821	£175	£300	£950	£1700
1821 proof	*	*	£1500	£3000
1822 (F)	£175	£300	£950	£1700
1823	£375	£1000	£3250	*
1824	£175	£300	£950	£1700
1825	£350	£950	£3250	*

Type bare head/shield

	F	VF	EF	Unc
1825 (F)	£200	£325	£850	£1425
1826	£200	£325	£850	£1425
1826 proof	*	*	£1200	£2500
1827 (F)	£200	£325	£850	£1425
1828 (F)	£1250	£3000	£10000	*
1829	£200	£355	£850	£1425
1830	£200	£325	£850	£1425

WILLIAM IV

	F	VF	EF	Unc
1831	£200	£375	£1100	£1800
1831 proof	*	*	£1500	£2750

William IV 1831 proof sovereign

	F	VF	EF	Unc
1832 (F)	£225	£350	£1000	£1600
1833	£225	£375	£1000	£1700
1835	£225	£350	£1000	£1650
1836	£225	£350	£1000	£1650
1837	£225	£350	£1000	£1700

VICTORIA
Type 1, YH obv, shield rev

	F	VF	EF	Unc
1838	£150	£475	£1250	£2500

Victoria 1839 proof sovereign

	F	VF	EF	Unc
1839	£150	£500	£1500	£4000
1839 proof	*	*	£1500	£3250
1841	£1000	£2000	£5250	*
1842	*	*	£250	£375
1843	*	*	£250	£375
1843 narrow shield	£2500	£4000	*	*
1844	*	*	£265	£375
1845	*	*	£265	£375
1846	*	*	£265	£375
1847	*	*	£265	£375
1848	*	*	£265	£375
1849	*	*	£265	£375
1850	*	*	£265	£375
1851	*	*	£265	£375
1852	*	*	£265	£375
1853	*	*	£250	£350

Victoria 1853 sovereign, shield on reverse

	F	VF	EF	Unc
1853 proof	*	*	£4000	£6500
1854	*	*	£200	£375
1855	*	*	£200	£375
1856	*	*	£200	£375
1857	*	*	£200	£375
1858	*	*	£200	£400
1859	*	*	£200	£325
1859 'Ansell' ...	£250	£750	£3250	*
1860	*	*	£200	£400
1861	*	*	£200	£350
1862	*	*	£180	£325
1863	*	*	£180	£325
1863 die number below wreath on rev	*	*	£180	£300
1863 '827' on truncation ...	£2500	£4000	*	*
1864 die no. ...	*	*	£160	£300
1865 die no. ...	*	*	£160	£300
1866 die no. ...	*	*	£160	£300
1868 die no. ...	*	*	£160	£300
1869 die no. ...	*	*	£160	£300
1870 die no. ...	*	*	£160	£300
1871 die no. ...	*	*	£160	£225
1871 S (Sydney mint) below wreath	*	*	£140	£600
1872	*	*	£140	£250
1872 die no. ...	*	*	£140	£225
1872 M (Melbourne mint) below wreath	*	*	£130	£450
1872 S	*	*	£250	£900
1873 die no. ...	*	*	£140	£250
1873 S	*	*	£120	£600
1874 die no. ...	£850	£2000	£4500	*
1874 M	*	*	£175	£800
1875 S	*	*	£150	£600
1877 S	*	*	£120	£450

	F	VF	EF	Unc
878 S	*	*	£110	£450
879 S	*	*	£110	£450
880 M	£200	£700	£1450	£3000
880 S	*	*	£120	£800
881 M	*	*	£150	£950
881 S	*	*	£120	£575
882 M	*	*	£120	£575
882 S	*	*	£120	£575
883 M	*	£150	£450	£1500
883 S	*	*	£110	£450
884 M	*	*	£110	£450
884 S	*	*	£110	£400
885 M	*	*	£110	£400
885 S	*	*	£110	£400
886 M	£400	£1750	£2750	£5000
886 S	*	*	£110	£450
887 M	£275	£500	£1750	£3750
887 S	*	*	£135	£575

Type II. YH obv, St George and Dragon rev

	F	VF	EF	Unc
871	*	*	£110	£200
871 S below head	*	£80	£250	£700
872	*	*	£110	£200
872 M below head	*	£110	£500	£2000
872 S	*	*	£150	£600
873	*	*	£100	£180
873 M	*	*	£150	£600
873 S	*	*	£200	£700
874	*	*	£110	£165
874 M	*	*	£200	£650
874 S	*	*	£150	£700
875 M	*	*	£110	£450
875 S	*	*	£150	£550
876	*	*	£110	£200
876 M	*	*	£110	£450
876 S	*	*	£150	£575
877 M	*	*	£10	£450
878	*	*	£110	£300
878 M	*	*	£110	£400
879	*	£275	£1250	*
879 M	*	*	£110	£450
879 S	*	*	£525	£1650
880	*	*	£100	£185
880 M	*	*	£110	£425
880 S	*	*	£110	£525
881 M	*	*	£110	£450
881 S	*	*	£110	£525
882 M	*	*	£110	£450
882 S	*	*	£110	£275
883 M	*	*	£110	£400
883 S	*	*	£135	£1000
1884	*	*	£95	£165
1884 M	*	*	£110	£375
1884 S	*	*	£110	£375
1885	*	*	£100	£185
1885 M	*	*	£110	£375
1885 S	*	*	£110	£300
1886 M	*	*	£110	£375
1886 S	*	*	£110	£425
1887 M	*	*	£110	£450
1887 S	*	*	£110	£300

Jubilee head coinage

	F	VF	EF	Unc
1887 (F)	*	*	£80	£100
1887 proof	*	*	£325	£500
1887 M on ground below dragon	*	*	£100	£250
1887 S on ground below dragon	*	*	£200	£850
1888	*	*	*	£100
1888 M	*	*	*	£250
1888 S	*	*	*	£225
1889	*	*	*	£100
1889 M	*	*	*	£165

SOVEREIGNS

	F	VF	EF	Unc
1889 S	*	*	*	£165
1890	*	*	*	£100
1890	*	*	*	£100
1890 S	*	*	*	£175
1891	*	*	*	£100
1891 M	*	*	*	£185
1891 S	*	*	*	£185
1892	*	*	*	£100
1892 M	*	*	*	£150
1892 S	*	*	*	£150
1893 M	*	*	*	£185
1893 S	*	*	*	£225

Old head coinage

	F	VF	EF	Unc
1893	*	*	*	£100
1893 proof	*	*	£375	£600
1893 M	*	*	*	£200
1893 S	*	*	*	£135
1894	*	*	*	£100
1894 M	*	*	*	£125
1894 S	*	*	*	£125
1895	*	*	*	£100
1895 M	*	*	*	£125
1895 S	*	*	*	£125
1896	*	*	*	£85
1896 M	*	*	*	£110
1896 S	*	*	*	£135
1897 M	*	*	*	£110
1897 S	*	*	*	£110
1898	*	*	*	£85
1898 M	*	*	*	£100
1898 S	*	*	*	£135
1899	*	*	*	£85

1898 Victoria Old Head sovereign

	F	VF	EF	Unc
1899 M	*	*	*	£100
1899 P (Perth mint) on ground below dragon	*	*	*	£900
1899 S	*	*	*	£125
1900	*	*	*	£100
1900 M	*	*	*	£100
1900 P	*	*	*	£150
1900 S	*	*	*	£125
1901	*	*	*	£100
1901 M	*	*	*	£100
1901 P	*	*	*	£165
1901 S	*	*	*	£120

EDWARD VII

	F	VF	EF	Unc
1902	*	*	*	£95
1902 proof	*	*	£125	£175
1902 M	*	*	*	£95
1902 P	*	*	*	£95
1902 S	*	*	*	£95
1903	*	*	*	£95
1903 M	*	*	*	£95
1903 P	*	*	*	£95
1903 S	*	*	*	£95
1904	*	*	*	£95
1904 M	*	*	*	£95
1904 P	*	*	*	£95
1904 S	*	*	*	£95
1905	*	*	*	£95
1905 M	*	*	*	£95
1905 P	*	*	*	£95

SOVEREIGNS

	F	VF	EF	Unc
1905 S	*	*	*	£95
1906	*	*	*	£95
1906 M	*	*	*	£95
1906 P	*	*	*	£95
1906 S	*	*	*	£95
1907	*	*	*	£95
1907 M	*	*	*	£95
1907 P	*	*	*	£95
1907 S	*	*	*	£95
1908	*	*	*	£95
1908 C (Canada, Ottawa mint) on ground below dragon (F)	*	*	£1750	£3000
1908 M	*	*	*	£95
1908 P	*	*	*	£95
1908 S	*	*	*	£95
1909	*	*	*	£95
1909 C	*	*	£125	£350
1909 M	*	*	*	£95
1909 P	*	*	*	£95
1909 S	*	*	*	£95
1910	*	*	*	£95
1910 C	*	*	£125	£300
1910 M	*	*	*	£95
1910 P	*	*	*	£95
1910 S	*	*	*	£95

GEORGE V

	F	VF	EF	Unc
1911	*	*	*	£85
1911 proof	*	*	£150	£325
1911 C	*	*	*	£135
1911 M	*	*	*	£80
1911 P	*	*	*	£80
1911 S	*	*	*	£80
1912	*	*	*	£80
1912 M	*	*	*	£80
1912 P	*	*	*	£80
1912 S	*	*	*	£80
1913	*	*	*	£80
1913 C (F)	*	£120	£400	£675
1913 M	*	*	*	£80
1913 P	*	*	*	£80
1913 S	*	*	*	£80
1914	*	*	*	£80
1914 C	*	£100	£225	£350
1914 M	*	*	*	£80
1914 P	*	*	*	£80
1914 S	*	*	*	£80
1915	*	*	*	£80
1915 M	*	*	*	£80
1915 P	*	*	*	£80
1915 S	*	*	*	£80
1916	*	*	*	£80
1916 C	*	£4000	£6500	*
1916 M	*	*	*	£80
1916 P	*	*	*	£80
1916 S	*	*	*	£80
1917 (F)	*	£2750	£4000	*
1917 C	*	*	£100	£140
1917 M	*	*	*	£80
1917 P	*	*	*	£80
1917 S	*	*	*	£80
1918 C	*	*	£100	£140
1918 I (Indian mint, Bombay), on ground below dragon	*	*	*	£80
1918 M	*	*	*	£80
1918 P	*	*	*	£80
1918 S	*	*	*	£80
1919 C	*	*	£100	£140
1919 M	*	*	*	£80
1919 P	*	*	*	£80
1919 S	*	*	*	£80
1920 M	*	£1150	£2000	£3000

	F	VF	EF	Unc
1920 P	*	*	*	£80
1920 S			highest	rarity
1921 M	*	£2750	£4750	£6000
1921 P	*	*	*	£80
1921 S	*	£350	£750	£1375
1922 M	*	£2250	£4000	£6500
1922 P	*	*	*	£85
1922 S	*	£2500	£6000	£850
1923 M	*	*	*	£85
1923 S	*	£2500	£5000	£7500
1923 SA (South Africa, Pretoria Mint) on ground below dragon	*	£1250	£1750	£3500
1924 M	*	*	£80	£100
1924 P	*	*	*	£85
1924 S	*	£450	£800	£1200
1924 SA	*	*	£2000	£3500
1925	*	*	*	£85
1925 M	*	*	*	£85
1925 P	*	*	£120	£200
1925 S	*	*	*	£85
1925 SA	*	*	*	£80
1926 M	*	*	*	£80
1926 P	*	£350	£700	£1350
1926 S	*	£5000	£8000	£12500
1926 SA	*	*	*	£80
1927 P	*	*	£225	£350
1927 SA	*	*	*	£80
1928 M	*	£800	£1300	£1900
1928 P	*	*	£85	£150
1928 SA	*	*	*	£80
1929 M	*	£500	£1200	£1700
1929 P	*	*	*	£80
1929 SA	*	*	*	£80
1930 M	*	*	£110	£175
1930 P	*	*	*	£80
1930 SA	*	*	*	£80
1931 M	*	£100	£175	£300
1931 P	*	*	*	£80
1931 SA	*	*	*	£80
1932 SA	*	*	*	£80

GEORGE VI

	F	VF	EF	Unc
1937 proof only			*	*	£700

ELIZABETH II

	F	VF	EF	Unc
1957	*	*	*	£80
1958	*	*	*	£80
1959	*	*	*	£80
1962	*	*	*	£80
1963	*	*	*	£80
1964	*	*	*	£80
1965	*	*	*	£80
1966	*	*	*	£80
1967	*	*	*	£80
1968	*	*	*	£80
1974	*	*	*	£80
1976	*	*	*	£80
1978	*	*	*	£80
1979	*	*	*	£80
1979 proof	*	*	*	£100
1980	*	*	*	£80
1980 proof	*	*	*	£95
1981	*	*	*	£80
1981 proof	*	*	*	£100
1982	*	*	*	£80
1982 proof	*	*	*	£100
1983 proof	*	*	*	£100
1984 proof	*	*	*	£100
1985 proof	*	*	*	£140
1986 proof	*	*	*	£140
1987 proof	*	*	*	£140
1988 proof	*	*	*	£150
1989 500th anniversary of the sovereign, proof	*	*	*	£400

SOVEREIGNS

	F	VF	EF	Unc
1990 proof	*	*	*	*
1991 proof	*	*	*	£175
1992 proof	*	*	*	£200
1993 proof	*	*	*	£200
1994 proof	*	*	*	£200
1995 proof	*	*	*	£200
1996 proof	*	*	*	£200
1997 proof	*	*	*	£200
1998 new portrait proof	*	*	*	£200
1999 proof	*	*	*	£250
2000				£85
2000 proof	*	*	*	£150
2001				£85
2001 proof	*	*	*	£135
2002 Shield reverse				£70
2002 Shield reverse, proof	*			£150
2003 Shield reverse, proof	*			£80
2003 proof	*	*	*	£150
2003 Ingot & sovereign	*			£135
2004 Forth Rail Bridge, proof	*			£345
2004 Forth Rail Bridge	*			£80
2004 proof Forth Rail Bridge				£135
2005 proof	*	*	*	£139
2005 proof	*	*	*	£80
2006 proof	*	*	*	£179

Half sovereigns

GEORGE III

	F	VF	EF	Unc
1817	£90	£150	£350	£600
1818	£90	£165	£350	£625
1820	£90	£165	£350	£625

GEORGE IV
Laureate head/ornate shield, date on rev

	F	VF	EF	Unc
1821	£350	£750	£1650	£2750
1821 proof	*	*	£1750	£3250
1823 plain shield	£85	£175	£400	£650
1824	£80	£145	£385	£600
1825	£80	£145	£385	£600

Bare head, date on obv/shield, full legend rev

	F	VF	EF	Unc
1826	£90	£150	£400	£625
1826 proof	*	*	£800	£1250
1827	£90	£150	£400	£625
1828	£100	£165	£425	£725

WILLIAM IV

	F	VF	EF	Unc
1831 proof	*	*	£1100	£1850
1834 reduced size	£110	£200	£650	£1000
1835 normal size	£110	£200	£550	£875
1836 sixpence oberse die				
	£750	£1500	£3500	£4000
1836	£125	£275	£600	£900
1837	£110	£225	£600	£900
1838	*	£100	£300	£575
1839 proof only	*	*	£900	£1650
1841	*	£100	£300	£600
1842	*	£90	£250	£500
1843	*	£100	£325	£575
1844	*	£100	£325	£525
1845	£100	£285	£1275	*
1846	*	£100	£325	£525
1847	*	£100	£325	£525
1848	*	£125	£325	£600
1849	*	£100	£250	£450
1850	£100	£275	£950	*
1851	*	£90	£225	£400
1852	*	£90	£225	£450
1853	*	£80	£200	£385
1853 proof	*	*	£2000	£3500
1854				Extremely rare
1855	*	£90	£200	£385
1856	*	£90	£200	£385
1857	*	£75	£225	£425
1858	*	£75	£225	£425
1859	*	£75	£200	£385
1860	*	£75	£200	£385
1861	*	£90	£200	£385
1862	£300	£825	£3250	*
1863	*	£90	£195	£385
1863 die no	*		£80	£275

	F	VF	EF	Unc
1864 die no.... ...	*	£75	£195	£325
1865 die no.... ...	*	£75	£195	£325
1866 die no.... ...	*	£75	£195	£325
1867 die no.... ...	*	£75	£195	£325
1869 die no.... ...	*	£75	£195	£325
1870 die no.... ...	*	£75	£195	£325
1871 die no. ...		£75	£195	£325
1871 S below shield	£80	£150	£600	£1750
1872 die no. ...	*	£75	£165	£325
1872 S	£80	£190	£550	£1650
1873 die no. ...	*	£75	£165	£325
1873 M below shield	£80	£200	£750	£1850
1874 die no. ...	*	*	*	£325
1875 die no. ...	*	*	*	£325
1875 S	*	*	£625	£1850
1876 die no. ...	*	*	£165	£325
1877 die no. ...	*	*	£145	£325
1877 M	£90	£200	£750	£2250
1878 die no. ...	*	*	£140	£295
1879 die no. ...	*	*	£140	£295
1879 S	£90	£200	£750	£2250
1880	*	*	£135	£275
1880 die no. ...	*	*	£135	£275
1880 S	£100	£175	£700	£2250
1881 S	£100	£175	£700	£2350
1881 M	£100	£175	£700	£2500
1882 S	£200	£600	£5500	£6000
1882 M	*	£120	£500	£2000
1883	*	*	£135	£250
1883 S	£80	£125	£525	£2000
1884	*	*	£110	£200
1884 M	£90	£200	£700	£1750
1885	*	*	£100	£200
1885 M	£200	£400	£1750	£3500
1886 S	*	£125	£700	£2000
1886 M	£90	£200	£850	£3000
1887 S	*	£100	£700	£1750
1887 M	£90	£300	£1750	£4250

Jubilee head/shield rev

	F	VF	EF	Unc
1887	*	*	£60	£100
1887 proof	*	*	£250	£400
1887 M	*	£100	£275	£875
1887 S	*	£100	£375	£875
1889 S	*	£150	£450	*
1890	*	*	£60	£100
1891	*	*	£50	£100
1891 S	*	*	£650	*
1892	*	*	£50	£100
1893	*	*	£50	£100
1893 M	*	*	£450	£1250

Old head/St George reverse

	F	VF	EF	Unc
1893	*	*	£45	£90
1893 proof	*	*	£225	£450
1893 M £1500		*	*	*
1893 S	*	£100	£275	£550
1894	*	*	£45	£90
1895	*	*	£45	£90
1896	*	*	£45	£90
1896 M	*	£100	£200	£350
1897	*	*	£40	£95
1897 S	*	£90	£250	£375
1898	*	*	£40	£95
1899	*	*	£40	£95
1899 M £70		£125	£375	£1375
1899 P proof only	*	*	*	ext. rare
1900	*	*	£40	£90
1900 M £70		£125	£375	*
1900 P £100		£250	£750	*
1900 S	*	£80	£350	£1275
1901	*	*	£40	£95
1901 P proof only	*	*	*	ext. rare

EDWARD VII

	F	VF	EF	Unc
1902	*	*	*	£60
1902 proof	*	*	£80	£110

1902
matt
proof
half
sovereign

	F	VF	EF	Unc
1902 S	*	*	£125	£125
1903	*	*	£50	£50
1903 S	*	*	£100	£100
1904	*	*	£50	£50
1904 P	£100	£200	£500	£500
1905	*	*	£50	£50
1906	*	*	£50	£50
1906 M	*	*	£375	£375
1906 S	*	*	£150	£150
1907	*	*	£50	£50
1907 M	*	*	£125	£125
1908	*	*	£50	£50
1908 M	*	*	£125	£125
1908 P	*	£100	£700	£700
1908 S	*	*	£125	£125
1909	*	*	£50	£50
1909 M	*	*	£150	£150
1909 P	*	£150	£500	£500
1910	*	*	£50	£50
1910 S	*	*	£100	£100

GEORGE V

	F	VF	EF	Unc
1911	*	*	*	£55
1911 proof	*	*	£100	£200
1911 P	*	*	£50	£150
1911 S	*	*	*	£95
1912	*	*	*	£55
1912 S	*	*	£50	£80
1913	*	*	*	£55
1914	*	*	*	£55
1914 S	*	*	*	£80
1915	*	*	*	£55
1915 M	*	*	£60	£100
1915 P	*	*	£100	£475
1915 S	*	*	*	£65
1916 S	*	*	*	£65
1918 P	*	£225	£625	£1250
1923 SA proof	*	*	*	£250
1925 SA	*	*	*	£55
1926 SA	*	*	*	£55

GEORGE VI

	F	VF	EF	Unc
1937 proof	*	*	*	£150

ELIZABETH II

	F	VF	EF	Unc
1980 proof	*	*	*	£60
1982	*	*	*	£60
1982 proof	*	*	*	£60
1983 proof	*	*	*	£60
1984 proof	*	*	*	£60
1985 proof	*	*	*	£80
1986 proof	*	*	*	£80
1987 proof	*	*	*	£80
1988 proof	*	*	*	£80
1989 500th anniversary of the sovereign, proof	*	*	*	£100
1990 proof	*	*	*	£80
1991 proof	*	*	*	£80
1992 proof	*	*	*	£90
1993 proof	*	*	*	£85
1994 proof	*	*	*	£85
1995 proof	*	*	*	£85
1996 proof	*	*	*	£85
1997 proof	*	*	*	£85
1998 new portrait proof	*	*	*	£85
1999 proof	*	*	*	£90
2000	*	*	*	£50
2000 proof	*	*	*	£70
2001	*	*	*	£50
2001 proof	*	*	*	£75
2002 shield reverse				£40
2002 shield reverse, proof				£75
2003				£40
2003 proof				£75
2004				£40
2004 proof				£75
2005 proof				£79
2005				£40

Crowns

CROMWELL

	F	VF	EF
1658	£1750	£2750	£4000
1658 Dutch copy	£1900	£2950	£5000
1658 Tanner's copy	*	£3250	£5500

CHARLES II

	F	VF	EF
1662 1st bust...	£125	£450	£3000
1663 –	£140	£550	£3000
1664 2nd bust	£140	£550	£3500
1665 –	£750	£1500	*
1666 –	£125	£550	£3500
1666 – eleph	£300	£1500	£7500
1667 –	£100	£400	£2500
1668 –	£95	£400	£2250
1668/7 –	£100	£450	£2750
1669 –	£275	£975	*
1669/8 –	£300	£900	*
1670 –	£100	£500	£2500
1670/69 –	£400	£700	*
1671 –	£100	£500	£2650
1671 3rd bust	£100	£450	£2500
1672 –	£100	£450	£2500
1673 –	£100	£450	£2500
1673/2 –	£125	£500	£3000
1674 –	*	*	ext rare
1675 –	£875	£3000	*
1675/4 –	£600	£2500	*
1676 –	£100	£300	£2000
1677 –	£100	£425	£2000
1677/6 –	£100	£425	£2000
1678/7 –	£120	£525	*
1679 –	£100	£425	£2000
1679 4th bust –	£125	£425	*
1680 3rd bust –	£140	£575	£2650
1680/79 –	£100	£475	£2500
1680 4th bust –	£110	£425	£2650
1680/79 –	£125	£500	*
1681 – elephant & castle ...	£2000	£3500	*
1681 –	£100	£400	£2650
1682 –	£125	£400	£2650
1682/1 –	£100	£400	£2650
1683 –	£175	£500	*
1684 –	£115	£450	*

JAMES II

	F	VF	EF
1686 1st bust...	£350	£1000	*
1687 2nd bust	£110	£500	£1750
1688 –	£135	£500	£1750
1688/7 –	£110	£500	£1750

WILLIAM AND MARY

	F	VF	EF
1691	£300	£800	£3250
1692	£325	£800	£3250
1692/2 inverted QVINTO... ...	£325	£800	£3250
1692/2 inverted QVARTO ...	£600	£1250	*

WILLIAM III

	F	VF	EF
1695 1st bust...	£95	£300	£1350
1696 –	£95	£300	£1350
1696 – GEI error...	£325	£800	*
1696/5 –	£200	£500	*
1696 2nd bust			unique
1696 3rd bust	£95	£300	£1350
1697	£700	£2250	£12500
1700 3rd bust variety	£95	£300	£1350

ANNE

	F	VF	EF
1703 1st bust VIGO	£250	£800	£2500
1705 –	£450	£1500	£3750
1706 –	£200	£475	£1650
1707 –	£175	£400	£1650
1707 2nd bust	£125	£375	£1375
1707 – E	£125	£375	£1375
1708 –	£125	£400	£1375

98

	F	VF	EF
1708 – E...	£125	£425	
1708/7 –	£125	£500	
1708 – plumes	£250	£475	£135...
1713 3rd bust	£250	£475	£135...

GEORGE I

	F	VF	EF
1716	£225	£600	£275...
1718	£300	£750	£275...
1718/6	£250	£650	£250...
1720	£250	£650	£250...
1720/18...	£225	£650	£250...
1723 SS C	£225	£650	£200...
1726 roses & plumes	£500	£1000	£375...

GEORGE II

	F	VF	EF
1732 YH	£225	£575	£170...
1732 – proof	*	*	£400...
1734 –	£225	£600	£187...
1735 –	£225	£600	£150...
1736 –	£225	£600	£150...
1739 –	£225	£525	£100...
1741	£225	£525	£100...
1743 OH	£200	£500	£100...

1691 William & Mary Crown

	F	VF	EF
1746 – LIMA	£300	£550	£1750
1746 – proof	*	*	£3000
1750	£300	£650	£1750
1751	£325	£675	£1950

GEORGE III

	F	VF	EF	Unc
Oval counter-stamp[1]	£200	£275	£550	*
Octagonal Counterstamp[1]	£400	£600	£1250	*
1804 Bank of England dollar[1]	£100	£150	£375	£650
1818 LVIII...	£10	£45	£250	£650
1818 – error edge	£250	*	*	*
1818 LIX	£10	£45	£250	£650

	F	VF	EF	Unc
1819 –	£10	£45	£250	£650
1819 – no edge stops	£50	£140	£400	*
1819/8 LIX	*	£150	£475	*
1819 LIX	£10	£50	£265	£650
1819 – no stop after TUTAMEN	£45	£150	£475	*
1820 LX	*	*	£300	£650
1820/19	£50	£200	£500	*

Beware of contemporary forgeries. The counter-stamps are usually on Spanish-American dollars.

GEORGE IV
	F	VF	EF	Unc
1821 1st hd SEC ...	£35	£150	£700	£1750
1821 – prf	*	*	*	£2750
1821 – TER error edge	*	*	*	£3500
1822 – SEC	£60	£200	£750	£1950
1822 – – prf	*	*	*	*
1822 – TER	£50	£175	£750	£1950
1822 – – prf	*	*	*	£3750
1823 – prf	*	*	*	ext.rare
1826 2nd hd prf	*	*	£2000	£3650

WILLIAM IV
	F	VF	EF	Unc
1831 w.w.	*	*	£5750	£9000
1831 w.wYON	*	*	£6750	£9500
1834 w.w.	*	*	£8750	£15000

VICTORIA
	F	VF	EF	Unc
1839 proof	*	*	£2500	£5000
1844 star stops	£25	£100	£750	£2250
1844 – prf	*	* ext.rare		*
1844 cinquefoil stops	£25	£100	£750	£2250
1845	£25	£100	£750	£2250
1845 proof	*	* ext.rare		*
1847	£25	£100	£850	£2500

Victoria 1847 Gothic crown

CROWNS

	F	VF	EF	Unc
1847 Gothic	£375	£600	£1250	£2250
1847 – plain edge ...	*	£675	£1350	£2650
1853 SEPTIMO	*	*	£4000	£6500
1853 plain	*	*	£4750	£8000
1887 JH	£12	£20	£60	£135
1887 – proof	*	*	£225	£450
1888 close date	£15	£25	£80	£200
1888 wide date	£25	£100	£375	£475
1889	£15	£35	£75	£175
1890	£15	£35	£75	£185
1891	£15	£35	£85	£200
1892	£15	£35	£100	£225
1893 LVI	£15	£35	£125	£300
1893 – proof	*	*	£225	£500
1893 LVII	£15	£65	£200	£425
1894 LVII	£15	£30	£125	£350
1894 LVIII	£15	£30	£125	£350
1895 LVIII...	£15	£30	£125	£350
1895 LIX	£15	£30	£125	£350
1896 LIX	£15	£50	£225	£450
1896 LX	£15	£30	£125	£350
1897 LX	£15	£30	£125	£350
1897 LXI	£15	£30	£120	£350
1898 LXI	£15	£30	£190	£425
1898 LXII	£15	£30	£145	£375
1899 LXII	£15	£39	£140	£350
1899 LXIII...	£15	£30	£140	£375
1900 LXIII...	£15	£30	£125	£375
1900 LXIV...	£15	£30	£120	£375

EDWARD VII
	F	VF	EF	Unc
1902	£20	£60	£110	£165
1902 matt proof	*	*	£110	£165

GEORGE V
	F	VF	EF	Unc
1927 proof	£35	£80	£145	£175
1928	£40	£100	£175	£300
1929	£40	£100	£175	£300
1930	£40	£110	£175	£300
1931	£40	£110	£175	£300
1932	£110	£185	£300	£475
1933	£45	£110	£175	£300
1934	£300	£600	£1350	£2250
1935	£5	£7	£10	£20
1935 rsd edge prf ...	*	*	*	£265
1935 gold proof	*	*	*	£15000
1935 prf in good silver (.925)	*	*	*	£1500
1935 specimen	*	*	*	£40
1936	£65	£90	£275	£375

GEORGE VI
	F	VF	EF	Unc
1937	*	*	£18	£25
1937 proof	*	*	*	£30
1937 'VIP' proof	*	*	*	£900
1951	*	*	*	£10
1951 'VIP' proof	*	*	*	£425

ELIZABETH II
	F	VF	EF	Unc
1953	*	*	*	£8
1953 proof	*	*	*	£30
1953 'VIP' proof	*	*	*	£350
1960	*	*	*	£8
1960 'VIP' proof	*	*	*	£400
1960 polished dies ...	*	*	*	£15
1965 Churchill	*	*	*	£1.00
1965 – 'satin' finish ...	*	*	*	£850

For issues 1972 onwards see under 25 pence in Decimal Coinage section.

George VI 1937 Crown (reverse)

Double florins

Cromwell 1658 halfcrown

Victoria 1887 halfcrown

VICTORIA

	F	VF	EF	Unc
1887 Roman 1	*	£15	£40	£90
1887 – proof	*	*	£150	£300
1887 Arabic 1	*	£15	£40	£90
1887 – proof	*	*	£125	£285
1888	*	£12	£45	£110
1888 inverted 1	£15	£30	£135	£350
1889	*	£10	£40	£95
1889 inverted 1	£15	£35	£135	£350
1890	*	£12	£50	£110

Three shilling bank tokens

Contemporary forgeries of these pieces, as well as of other George III coins, were produced in quite large numbers. Several varieties exist for the pieces dated 1811 and 1812. Prices given here are for the commonest types of these years.

GEORGE III

	F	VF	EF	Unc
1811	*	£35	£95	£140
1812 draped bust ...	*	£35	£95	£140
1812 laureate head	*	£35	£95	£140
1813	*	£35	£95	£140
1814	*	£35	£95	£140
1815	*	£35	£95	£140
1816	£10	*	£250	£600 £1200

Halfcrowns

CROMWELL

	F	VF	EF
1656	£1650	£3000	*)
1658	£800	£1500	£2750)

CHARLES II

	F	VF	EF
1663 1st bust	£100	£500	£3000
1664 2nd bust	£125	£600	£3500
1666/3 3rd bust	£750	*	*
1666/3 – elephant	£750	£1850	*
1667/4 –	ext.rare		
1668/4 –	£175	£700	*
1669 –	£275	£1100	*
1669/4 –	£200	£750	*
1670 –	£65	£375	£2500
1671 3rd bust var	£65	£375	£2500
1671/0 –	£95	£500	£2750
1672 –	£80	£425	£2500
1672 4th bust	£100	£400	£2500
1673 –	£65	£300	£2500
1673 – plume below	£1750	*	*
1673 – plume both sides ...	ext. rare		
1674 –	£125	£400	*
1674/3 –	£250	£700	*
1675 –	£80	£350	£2000
1676 –	£80	£350	£2000
1677 –	£80	£350	£2000
1678 –	£175	£650	*
1679 –	£80	£350	£1850
1680 –	£150	£450	*
1681 –	£80	£350	£2250
1681/0 –	£150	£400	£2250
1681 – eleph & castle	£2000	£5250	*
1682 –	£100	£425	*
1682/1 –	£150	£600	*
1682/79 –	ext. rare		
1683 –	£70	£350	£2000
1683 – plume below	ext. rare	*	*
1684/3 –	£175	£750	*

James III 1687 halfcrown

JAMES II

	F	VF	EF
1685 1st bust	£110	£525	£2250
1686 –	£110	£525	£2000
1686/5 –	£200	£850	*
1687 –	£110	£525	£2000

100

	F	VF	EF
1687/6 –	£525	£525	£2000
1687 2nd bust	£125	£525	£2000
1688 –	£100	£475	£2000

WILLIAM AND MARY

	F	VF	EF
1689 1st busts 1st shield ...	£60	£350	£1450
1689 – 2nd shield	£60	£350	£1450
1690 – –	£75	£400	£2250
1691 2nd busts 3rd shield ...	£65	£375	£1450
1692 – –	£65	£325	£1450
1693 – –	£60	£350	£1450
1693 – – 3 inverted	£85	£550	£1850
1693 3 over 3 inverted	£80	£400	£1400

William and Mary 1693 Halfcrown

WILLIAM III

	F	VF	EF
1696 large shield early harp	£50	£250	£700
1696 – – B	£60	£250	£750
1696 – – C	£65	£250	£750
1696 – – E	£85	£325	£875
1696 – – N	£125	£450	£1500
1696 – – Y	£60	£275	£800
1696 – – y/E	ext rare	*	*
1696 – ord harp	£100	£475	£1200
1696 – – C	£110	£425	£1350
1696 – – E	£120	£425	£1200
1696 – – N	£120	£450	£1500
1696 small shield	£45	£225	£800
1696 – B	£80	£250	£800
1696 – C	£100	£275	£825
1696 – E	£200	£475	£1100
1696 – N	£110	£400	£1350
1696 – y	£110	£300	£925
1696 2nd bust			unique
1697 1st bust large shield ...	£40	£200	£750
1697 – – B	£65	£275	£850
1697 – – C	£70	£275	£800
1697 – – E	£50	£250	£800
1697 – – E/C	£125	*	*
1697 – – N	£65	£295	£875
1697 – – y	£65	£275	£800

1697 Halfcrown of NORWICH: N below bust

	F	VF	EF
1698 – –	£40	£225	£750
1699 – –	£80	£300	£1000

	F	VF	EF
1700 – –	£40	£165	£675
1701 – –	£50	£1850	£750
1701 – eleph & castle	£2500	*	*
1701 – plumes	£200	£575	£2500

ANNE

	F	VF	EF
1703 plain	£700	£1750	£9000
1703 VIGO	£150	£300	£1000
1704 plumes	£250	£600	*
1705 –	£150	£375	£1350
1706 r & p	£90	£275	£900
1707 –	£60	£275	£900
1707 plain	£50	£200	£650
1707 E	£50	£200	£800
1708 plain	£40	£200	£650
1708 E	£50	£275	£900
1708 plumes	£95	£325	£1100
1709 plain	£45	£250	£750
1709 E	£400	*	*
1710 r & p	£75	£275	£875
1712 –	£45	£200	£675
1713 plain	£75	£300	£725
1713 r & p	£60	£275	£850
1714 –	£50	£275	£850
1714/3	£125	£400	£1150

GEORGE I

	F	VF	EF
1715 proof	*	*	£5000
1715 r & p	£125	£400	£2200
1717 –	£150	£450	£2250
1720 –	£275	£650	£2500
1720/17 –	£125	£450	£2200
1723 SS C	£100	£375	£1650
1726 small r & p	£2500	£4500	£12500

Spanish Half Dollar with George III counterstamp (octagonal)

GEORGE II

	F	VF	EF
1731 YH proof	*	£1750	£4000
1731	£85	£325	£1000
1732	£85	£325	£1050
1734	£85	£325	£1050
1735	£85	£325	£1050
1736	£85	£325	£1100
1739	£70	£225	£800
1741	£90	£275	£875
1741/39	£85	£250	£950
1743 OH	£70	£195	£775
1745	£60	£145	£850
1745 LIMA	£50	£165	£850
1746 -	£50	£165	£550
1746 plain, proof	*	*	£1650
1750	£90	£375	£1100
1751	£80	£425	£1350

GEORGE III	F	VF	EF	Unc
Oval counterstamp usually on Spanish half dollar	£175	£300	£5500	*

HALFCROWNS

	F	VF	EF	Unc
1816 large head	*	£50	£200	£425
1817 –	*	£50	£200	£425
1817 small head ...	*	£50	£200	£425
1818	*	£50	£225	£475
1819	*	£50	£200	£475
1819/8	*	*	*	*
1820	*	£60	£250	£475

George IV halfcrown of 1821

GEORGE IV

	F	VF	EF	Unc
1820 1st hd 1st rev ...	*	£50	£185	£425
1821 –	*	£50	£185	£425
1821 proof	*	*	£600	£1100
1823	£750	£1750	£5000	*
1823 – 2nd rev ...	*	£50	£195	£450
1824 – –	£25	£70	£225	£600
1824 2nd hd 3rd rev ...				ext.rare
1825 – –	*	£70	£125	£400
1826 – –	*	£25	£125	£400
1826 – – proof ...	*	*	£400	£700
1828 – –	*	£35	£225	£600
1829 – –	*	£35	£190	£500

William IV 1831 halfcrown

WILLIAM IV

	F	VF	EF	Unc
1831		Extremely rare		
1831 proof	*	*	£575	£900
1834 ww	£30	£110	£450	£875
1834 ww in script ...	£12	£40	£200	£475
1835	£25	£80	£300	£625
1836	£12	£50	£200	£475
1836/5	£30	£100	£450	*
1837	£35	£90	£375	£800

VICTORIA

From time to time halfcrowns bearing dates ranging from 1861 to 1871 are found, but except for rare proofs: 1853, 1862 and 1864, no halfcrowns were struck between 1850 and 1874, so pieces dated for this period are now considered to be contemporary or later forgeries.

	F	VF	EF	Unc
1839 plain and ornate fillets, ww	*	£975	£3500	
1839 – plain edge proof	*	*	£600	£1000
1839 plain fillets, ww incuse	*	£1250	£3500	*
1840	£15	£75	£400	£800
1841	£75	£225	£1500	£2850
1842	£15	£40	£375	£800
1843	£50	£125	£600	£1100
1844	£15	£40	£375	£675
1845	£15	£40	£375	£675
1846	£20	£50	£350	£675
1848	£75	£175	£800	£1850
1848/6	£75	£200	£750	£1500
1849 large date	£25	£85	£475	£925
1849 small date	£50	£175	£500	£1050
1850	£25	£85	£425	£925
1853 proof	*	*	£800	£1750
1862 proof	*	*	*	£4000
1864 proof	*	*	*	£4000
1874	*	£30	£110	£350
1875	*	£25	£110	£350
1876	*	£35	£130	£375
1876/5	*	£50	£275	£550
1877	*	£25	£110	£350
1878	*	£25	£110	£350
1879	*	£35	£145	£375
1880	*	£25	£120	£350
1881	*	£25	£120	£350
1882	*	£25	£140	£325
1883	*	£25	£110	£325
1884	*	£25	£110	£325
1885	*	£25	£120	£300
1886	*	£25	£110	£300
1887 YH	*	£25	£135	£300
1887 JH	*	£15	£25	£65
1887 – proof	*	*	£85	£150
1888	*	£20	£55	£120
1889	*	£20	£55	£130
1890	*	£25	£60	£135
1891	*	£25	£60	£135
1892	*	£25	£55	£135
1893 OH	*	£20	£30	£135
1893 – proof	*	*	£90	£175
1894	*	£20	£55	£140
1895	*	£20	£50	£125
1896	*	£20	£45	£125
1897	*	£15	£50	£125
1898	*	£20	£50	£135
1899	*	£20	£50	£125
1900	*	£20	£50	£125
1901	*	£20	£45	£125

EDWARD VII

	F	VF	EF	Unc
1902	*	£20	£45	£90
1902 matt proof	*	*	*	£110
1903	£50	£120	£700	£1200
1904	£35	£90	£500	£975
1905 (F)	£150	£500	£1850	£3750
1906	*	£30	£165	£475
1907	*	£40	£165	£475
1908	*	£40	£350	£725
1909	*	£25	£300	£600
1910	*	£20	£130	£375

GEORGE V

	F	VF	EF	Unc
1911	*	£110	£40	£100
1911 proof	*	*	*	£85
1912	*	£14	£60	£150
1913	*	£14	£65	£165
1914	*	*	£20	£70
1915	*	*	£15	£65
1916	*	*	£15	£65

	F	VF	EF	Unc
1917	*	*	£30	£75
1918	*	*	£20	£60
1919	*	*	£20	£60
1920	*	*	£20	£80
1921	*	*	£25	£85
1922	*	*	£20	£85
1923	*	*	£12	£40
1924	*	*	£25	£60
1925	£12	£25	£245	£500

George V 1926 halfcrown

1926	*	*	£30	£100
1926 mod eff	*	*	£35	£95
1927	*	*	£20	£50
1927 new rev, proof only	*	*	*	£45
1928	*	*	£10	£25
1929	*	*	£10	£20
1930	£7	£35	£125	£300
1931	*	*	£10	£20
1932	*	*	£15	£35
1933	*	*	£9	£20
1934	*	*	£20	£45
1935	*	*	£6	£14
1936	*	*	£6	£12

GEORGE VI

1937	*	*	*	£12
1937 proof	*	*	*	£18
1938	*	*	£4	£25
1939	*	*	*	£17
1940	*	*	*	£12
1941	*	*	*	£12
1942	*	*	*	£9
1943	*	*	*	£12
1944	*	*	*	£9
1945	*	*	*	£9
1946	*	*	*	£7
1947	*	*	*	£7
1948	*	*	*	£7
1949	*	*	*	£12
1950	*	*	*	£15
1950 proof	*	*	*	£18
1951	*	*	*	£18
1951 proof	*	*	*	£18

ELIZABETH II

1953	*	*	*	£10
1953 proof	*	*	*	£12
1954	*	*	£3	£35
1955	*	*	*	£9
1956	*	*	*	£9
1957	*	*	*	£6
1958	*	*	£3	£20
1959	*	*	£4	£45
1960	*	*	*	£4
1961	*	*	*	£2
1962	*	*	*	£4
1963	*	*	*	£2
1964	*	*	*	£2
1965	*	*	*	£2
1966	*	*	*	£1
1967	*	*	*	£1

Florins

The first florins produced in the reign of Victoria bore the legend VICTORIA REGINA and the date, omitting DEI GRATIA (By the Grace of God). They are therefore known as 'Godless' florins.

The date of a Victorian Gothic florin is shown in Roman numerals, in Gothic lettering on the obverse for example: mdccclvii (1857). Gothic florins were issued during the period 1851-1887.

VICTORIA	F	VF	EF	Unc
1848 'Godless' proof with milled edge	*	*	*	£1750
1848 'Godless' proof with plain edge	*	*	*	£750

Victoria 1849 'Godless' florin

1849 – ww obliterated by circle	£25	£50	£190	£375
1849 – ww inside circle	£15	£40	£140	£250
1851 proof only	*	*	*	£7500
1852	£15	£40	£135	£300
1853	£15	£40	£135	£300
1853 no stop after date	£20	£50	£150	£375
1853 proof	*	*	*	£1650
1854	£250	£700	£3000	*
1855	*	£35	£165	£375
1856	*	£50	£185	£395
1857	*	£40	£165	£325
1858	*	£40	£165	£325
1859	*	£40	£165	£325
1859 no stop after date	*	£50	£175	£325
1860	*	£50	£200	£375
1862	£40	£200	£1500	*
1863	£80	£300	£2000	*
1864	*	£40	£175	£325
1865	*	£40	£225	£450
1865 colon after date	*	£50	*	*
1866	*	£50	£175	£375
1866 colon after date	*	£55	*	*
1867	£15	£70	£185	£375
1868	*	£50	£225	£475
1869	*	£45	£225	£450
1870	*	£40	£150	£300
1871	*	£40	£165	£325

Victoria 1859 Gothic florin

FLORINS

	F	VF	EF	Unc
1872	*	£35	£135	£275
1873	*	£35	£145	£300
1874	*	£35	£165	£365
1874 xxiv/iii - (die	£75	£175	£400	*
1875	*	£45	£150	£325
1876	*	£45	£150	£325
1877	*	£45	£150	£325
1877 no ww	*	*	*	*
1877 42 arcs	*	*	*	*
1878	*	£40	£150	£325
1879 ww 48 arcs	*	£40	£150	£325
1879 die no.	*	*	*	*
1879 ww. 42 arcs	£12	£40	£150	£300
1879 no ww, 38 arcs	*	£45	£150	£300
1880	*	£40	£150	£300
1881	*	£40	£150	£300
1881 xxri	*	£40	£150	£300
1883	*	£40	£140	£250
1884	*	£40	£140	£250
1885	*	£40	£140	£250
1886	*	£40	£140	£250
1887 33 arcs	*	*	*	*
1887 46 arcs	*	£40	£200	£400
1887 JH	*	£10	£25	£45
1887 – proof	*	*	*	£120
1888	*	£10	£40	£95
1889	*	£10	£45	£110
1890	£8	£15	£70	£200
1891	£20	£50	£165	£400
1892	£20	£50	£125	£350
1893 OH	*	£12	£45	£90
1893 proof	*	*	*	£120
1894	*	£12	£60	£125
1895	*	£12	£50	£100
1896	*	£12	£45	£100
1897	*	£12	£45	£100
1898	*	£12	£45	£100
1899	*	£12	£45	£100
1900	*	£12	£45	£100
1901	*	£12	£45	£100

Edward VII 1902 florin

EDWARD VII

	F	VF	EF	Unc
1902	*	£12	£40	£75
1902 matt proof	*	*	*	£65
1903	*	£25	£100	£300
1904	*	£32	£125	£325
1905	£35	£125	£475	£900
1906	*	£20	£95	£300
1907	*	£25	£90	£300
1908	*	£30	£170	£475
1909	*	£25	£150	£375
1910	*	£15	£75	£175

GEORGE V

	F	VF	EF	Unc
1911	*	*	£30	£85
1911 proof	*	*	*	£70
1912	*	*	£40	£95
1913	*	*	£60	£145
1914	*	*	£25	£50
1915	*	*	£30	£55
1916	*	*	£20	£65
1917	*	*	£25	£55
1918	*	*	£20	£50
1919	*	*	£25	£55
1920	*	*	£25	£65
1921	*	*	£20	£75
1922	*	*	£18	£50
1923	*	*	£18	£50
1924	*	*	£18	£40
1925	£15	£35	£125	£275
1926	*	*	£30	£80
1927 proof only	*	*		£50

George V 1928 florin

	F	VF	EF	Unc
1928	*	*	£7	£20
1929	*	*	£7	£20
1930	*	*	£10	£20
1931	*	*	£8	£20
1932	£15	£60	£150	£300
1933	*	*	£8	£20
1935	*	*	£8	£18
1936	*	*	£5	£18

GEORGE VI

	F	VF	EF	Unc
1937	*	*	*	£7
1937 proof	*	*	*	£15
1938	*	*	£4	£25
1939	*	*	*	£12
1940	*	*	*	£10
1941	*	*	*	£10
1942	*	*	*	£8
1943	*	*	*	£8
1944	*	*	*	£8
1945	*	*	*	£8
1946	*	*	*	£8
1947	*	*	*	£8
1948	*	*	*	£8
1949	*	*	*	£12
1950	*	*	*	£12
1950 proof	*	*	*	£12
1951	*	*	*	£15
1951 proof	*	*	*	£20

George VI 1949 florin

ELIZABETH II	F	VF	EF	Unc
1953	*	*	*	£6
1953 proof	*	*	*	£10
1954	*	*	*	£45
1955	*	*	*	£5
1956	*	*	*	£5
1957	*	*	*	£45
1958	*	*	*	£20
1959	*	*	*	£35
1960	*	*	*	£3
1961	*	*	*	£3
1962	*	*	*	£2
1963	*	*	*	£2
1964	*	*	*	£2
1965	*	*	*	£2
1966	*	*	*	£1
1967	*	*	*	£1

One and sixpence bank tokens

GEORGE III	F	VF	EF	Unc
1811	£9	£25	£70	£110
1812 laureate bust ...	£9	£25	£75	£120
1812 laureate head	£9	£25	£75	£120
1813	£9	£25	£75	£120
1814	£9	£25	£75	£120
1815	£9	£25	£75	£120
1816	£9	£25	£75	£120

Shillings

1658 shilling of Cromwell

CROMWELL	F	VF	EF
1658	£400	£800	£1750
1658 Dutch copy	*	*	*

Charles II 1671 shilling, plumes below bust

CHARLES II	F	VF	EF
1663 1st bust	£80	£275	£900
1663 1st bust var	£80	£275	£850
1666 –	*	*	*
1666 – eleph	£350	£1250	£4000
1666 guinea hd, eleph ...	£2000	*	*

	F	VF	EF
1666 2nd bust	£1350	*	*
1668 1st bust var	£375	£1375	*
1668 2nd bust	£50	£275	£825
1668/7 –	£90	£350	£1250
1669/6 1st bust var ... ... ext. rare		*	*
1669 2nd bust ... ... ext. rare		*	*
1670 –	£85	£400	£1200
1671 –	£95	£425	£1350
1671 – plumes both sides	£425	£900	*
1672 –	£70	£350	£975
1673 –	£70	£400	£1350
1673/2 –	£80	£500	£1600
1673 – plumes both sides	£425	£950	£2750
1674 –	£70	£475	£1350
1674/3 –	£70	£425	£1150
1674 – plumes both sides	£425	£950	£2750
1674 – plumes rev only ...	£425	£1250	£3250
1674 3rd bust	£300	£900	*
1675 –	£350	£900	*
1675/3 –	£350	£900	*
1675 2nd bust	£250	£625	*
1675/4 –	£250	£625	*
1675 – plumes both sides	£425	£950	£2750
1676	£65	£325	£975
1676/5 –	£70	£375	£1000
1676 – plumes both sides	£425	£950	£2750
1677 –	£60	£350	£925
1677 – plume obv only ...	£500	£1500	£3650
1678 –	£70	£400	£1025
1678/7 –	£70	£400	£1025
1679 –	£60	£350	£975
1679/7 –	£70	£350	£1025
1679 plumes	£425	£950	£2750
1679 plumes obv only ...	£575	£1200	£3650
1680 –		Extremely rare	
1680 plumes	£425	£1000	£3000
1680/79 –	£425	£1000	£3000
1681 –	£100	£450	£1250
1681/0	£100	£450	£1250
1681/0 – eleph & castle ...	£1950	*	*
1682/1	£475	£1200	*
1683 – ... ... Ext rare		*	*
1683 4th bust	£125	£550	£1750
1684 –	£110	£500	£1750

James II 1685 shilling

JAMES II	F	VF	EF
1685 –	£125	£375	£1425
1685 no stops on rev	£175	£600	£1850
1685 plume on rev		Extremely Rare	
1686	£125	£400	£1250
1686 V/S	£125	£425	£1375
1687	£125	£400	£1250
1687/6	£125	£375	£1250
1688	£125	£400	£1375
1688/7	£125	£400	£1375
WILLIAM & MARY			
1692	£125	£450	£1500
1693	£125	£450	£1400

SHILLINGS

WILLIAM III	F	VF	EF
1695	£25	£100	£500
1696	£25	£90	£375
1696 no stops on rev ...	£40	£175	£650
1669 in error	£750	*	*
1696 1st bust B	£35	£135	£550
1696 – C	£35	£135	£550
1696 – E	£35	£135	£550
1696 – N	£35	£135	£550
1696 – Y	£35	£135	£550
1696 – Y	£40	£165	£650
1696 2nd bust		unique	
1696 3rd bust C	£145	£375	£975
1696 – E		Extremely rare	
1697 1st bust	£25	£90	£375
1697 – no stops on rev ...	£75	£200	£650
1697 – B	£45	£135	£525
1697 – C	£40	£135	£525

1697 Shilling of BRISTOL: B below bust

1697 – E	£40	£135	£525
1697 – N	£40	£135	£525
1697 – y	£40	£135	£525
1697 – Y	£40	£135	£550
1697 3rd bust	£25	£85	£375
1697 – B	£40	£135	£525
1697 – C	£30	£125	£450
1697 – E	£40	£135	£525
1697 – N	£40	£135	£525
1697 – y	£35	£135	£525
1697 3rd bust var	£20	£90	£375
1697 – B	£30	£110	£500
1697 – C	£120	£325	£850
1698	£35	£135	£525
1698 – plumes	£165	£450	£1200
1698 4th bust	£85	£325	£1100
1699 –	£90	£325	£1100
1699 5th bust	£80	£300	£750
1699 – plumes	£50	£400	£1575
1699 – roses	£50	£400	£1575
1700 –	£30	£90	£350
1700 – no stops on rev ...	£55	£150	£425
1700 – plume	£2000	*	*
1701 –	£65	£200	£525
1701 – plumes	£120	£325	£1250

Anne 1702 shilling, VIGO below bust

ANNE			
1702 – 1st bust	£70	£250	£650

1702 – plumes	£75	£275	£700
1702 – VIGO	£60	£250	£575
1703 2nd bust VIGO	£60	£200	£500
1704 –	£385	£1250	*
1704 – plumes	£80	£325	£800
1705 –	£80	£300	£725
1705 – plumes	£75	£250	£650
1705 – r&p	£70	£225	£550
1707 – r&p	£70	£225	£550
1707 – E	£60	£165	£550
1707 – E★	£90	£300	£650
1707 3rd bust	£25	£145	£400
1707 – plumes	£40	£185	£500
1707 – E	£30	£110	£450
1707 Edin bust E★	£350	*	*
1708 2nd bust E	£80	£300	£700
1708 – E★	£70	£225	£575
1708/7 – E★		Extremely rare	
1708 – r&p	£125	£325	£00
1708 3rd bust	£30	£85	£325
1708 – plumes	£50	£150	£500
1708 – r&p	£80	£300	£700
1708 – E	£85	£275	£700
1708 – E	£110	£300	£800
1708 – Edin bust E★	£80	£225	£625
1709 –	£50	£100	£400
1709 - Edin bust E	£250	£850	*
1709 - Edin bust E *... ...	£90	£285	£725
1710 – r&p	£45	£190	£475
1710 4th bust prf		Extremely rare	
1710 – r&p	£50	£185	£500
1711 3rd bust	£175	£475	£1100
1711 4th bust	£20	£85	£250
1712 – r&p	£30	£125	£375
1713/2 –	£50	£165	£400
1714 –	£35	£150	£400
1714/3 –		Extremely rare	

George I 1723 SS C shilling

GEORGE I			
1715 1st bust r&p	£35	£145	£550
1716 –	£100	£325	£925
1717 –	£35	£145	£550
1718 –	£45	£125	£500
1719 –	£95	£300	£825
1720 –	£45	£145	£550
1720 – plain	£35	£125	£475
1720 – large 0	£35	£145	£500
1721 –	£175	£500	£1100
1721 r&p	£35	£145	£600
1721/0 –	£35	£125	£550
1721/19 –	£40	£150	£625
1721/18 –		ext.rare	*
1722 –	£35	£145	£550
1723 –	£35	£145	£550
1723 – SS C	£30	£80	£300
1723 - SSC - C/SS	£35	£110	£325
1723 - SSC Fench arms at date...	£125	£400	£1250
1723 2nd bust SS C...	£50	£120	£325
1723 - r&p	£50	£165	£500
1723 - w.c.c...	£375	£800	£2500
1724 - r&p	£50	£165	£500
1724 - w.c.c	£375	£800	£2500

	F	VF	EF
1725 – r & p	£50	£165	£500
1725 – no obv stops	£75	£250	£650
1725 – w.c.c.	£425	£900	£2650
1726 – r & p	£500	£1100	*
1726 – w.c.c.	£450	£875	£2500
1727 – r & p	£500	*	*
1727 – – no stops on obv	£450	£1200	*

GEORGE II

	F	VF	EF
1727 YH plumes	£85	£350	£825
1727 – r & p	£50	£165	£625
1728 –	£150	£395	£975
1728 – r & p	£70	£200	£675
1729 – –	£80	£200	£675
1731 – –	£60	£165	£625
1731 – plumes	£120	£400	£1100
1732 – r & p	£70	£200	£675
1734 – –	£50	£150	£550
1735 – –	£50	£150	£550
1736 – –	£50	£150	£550
1736/5 – –	£70	£185	£650
1737 – –	£50	£145	£550
1739 – roses	£25	£125	£475
1741 – roses	£25	£125	£475

1763 'Northumberland' Shilling

	F	VF	EF
'1743 OH roses	£25	£80	£425
'1745 –	£30	£95	£450
'1745 – LIMA	£20	£75	£425
'1746 – – LIMA	£80	£225	£700
'1746/5 – LIMA	£110	£300	£750
'1746 – proof	*	£600	£1000
'1747 – roses	£35	£385	£395
'1750 –	£45	£150	£550
'1750/6 –	£50	£185	£600
'1751 –	£80	£225	£700
'1758 –	£15	£40	£75

1728 Young Head Shilling

GEORGE III

	F	VF	EF	Unc
1763 'Northumberland'	£225	£450	£750	£1150
1786 proof or pattern	*	*	*	£5000
1787 no hearts	£15	£25	£70	£150
1787 – no stop over head	£20	£40	£100	£200
1787 – no stops at date	£20	£50	£150	£250

	F	VF	EF	Unc
1787 – no stops on obv	£250	£600	*	*
1787 hearts	£15	£25	£70	£150
1798 'Dorrien and Magens'	*	£4250	£7000	£9500
1816	*	£5	£60	£110
1817	*	£5	£65	£110
1817 GEOE	£50	£125	£450	*
1818	£4	£25	£125	£250
1819	*	£4	£75	£125
1819/8	*	*	£120	£225
1820	*	£4	£65	£145

GEORGE IV

	F	VF	EF	Unc
1820 1st hd 1st rev pattern or prf	*	*	*	£4000
1821 1st hd 1st rev	£10	£30	£150	£325
1821 – proof	*	*	£450	£750
1823 – 2nd rev	£20	£50	£250	£575
1824 – –	£8	£35	£150	£325
1825 – –	£15	£40	£150	£375
1825 2nd hd	£10	£25	£120	£275
1826 –	*	£25	£110	£245

George IV 1824 shilling

	F	VF	EF	Unc
1826 – proof	*	*	£200	£375
1827	£10	£50	£250	£525
1829	*	£40	£175	£425

WILLIAM IV

	F	VF	EF	Unc
1831 proof	*	*	*	£500
1834	£10	£30	£150	£350
1835	£10	£35	£165	£375
1836	£15	£25	£165	£350
1837	£25	£75	£200	£525

William IV 1837 shilling

VICTORIA

	F	VF	EF	Unc
1838	£8	£18	£135	£300
1839	£8	£20	£135	£300
1839 2nd YH	£8	£20	£135	£300
1839 – proof	*	*	*	£475
1840	£12	£35	£150	£325
1841	£12	£35	£150	£325
1842	£10	£20	£100	£250
1843	£12	£30	£150	£300
1844	£8	£20	£100	£225
1845	£8	£20	£110	£275
1846	£8	£20	£100	£225
1848/6	£40	£125	£525	£850
1849	£12	£25	£110	£275

SHILLINGS

	F	VF	EF	Unc
1850	£200	£800	£1650	*
1850/46	£200	£800	£1750	*
1851	£40	£150	£450	£875
1852	£8	£20	£85	£200
1853	£8	£20	£85	£200
1853 proof	*	*	*	£425
1854	£75	£300	£975	*
1855	£8	£20	£80	£200
1856	£8	£20	£80	£200
1857	£8	£20	£80	£200
1857 F:G:	£200	*	*	*
1858	£8	£20	£85	£200
1859	£8	£20	£85	£200
1860	£10	£25	£130	£275
1861	£10	£25	£120	£275
1862	£15	£35	£165	£325

Victoria 1839 shilling

	F	VF	EF	Unc
1863	£15	£50	£300	£700
1863/1	£60	£150	£500	*
1864	£8	£15	£85	£200
1865	£8	£15	£85	£200
1866	£8	£15	£85	£200
1866 BBITANNIAR ...	*	*	£450	*
1867	£8	£15	£90	£200
1867 3rd YH, die no. :	£150	£325	*	*
1868	£8	£20	£100	£200
1869	£12	£30	£100	£225
1870	£10	£25	£100	£200
1871	£8	£20	£95	£195
1872	£8	£20	£95	£195
1873	£8	£20	£95	£195
1874	£8	£20	£95	£195
1875	£8	£20	£95	£195
1876	£10	£25	£95	£195
1877 die no.	£8	£20	£95	£195
1877 no die no	*	*	*	*
1878	£8	£20	£95	£195
1879 3rd YH	£45	£100	£250	*
1879 4th YH	£8	£20	£85	£165
1880	£6	£15	£70	£150
1880 longer line below SHILLING	*	*	*	*
1881	£6	£15	£70	£150
1881 longer line below SHILLING	£6	£15	£70	£150
1881 – Large rev lettering	£6	£15	£70	£145
1882	£10	£35	£120	£225
1883	£6	£15	£60	£145
1884	£6	£15	£60	£145
1885	£6	£15	£60	£145
1886	£6	£15	£60	£145
1887	£7	£25	£110	£210
1887 JH	*	*	£12	£35
1887 proof	*	*	*	£95
1888	*	£6	£40	£70
1889	£40	£100	£300	*
1889 large JH	*	*	£40	£70
1890	*	*	£40	£80
1891	*	*	£40	£80
1892	*	*	£40	£80

Victoria Jubilee Head and Old Head shillings

	F	VF	EF	Unc
1893 OH	*	*	£35	£60
1893 – proof	*	*	*	£100
1893 small obv letters	*	*	£40	£75
1894	*	*	£45	£75
1895	*	*	£40	£70
1896	*	*	£40	£70
1897	*	*	£40	£70
1898	*	*	£40	£70
1899	*	*	£40	£70
1900	*	*	£40	£70
1901	*	*	£40	£60

EDWARD VII

	F	VF	EF	Unc
1902	*	*	£40	£60
1902 matt prf	*	*	£40	£60

Edward VII 1905 shilling

	F	VF	EF	Unc
1903	*	£15	£100	£350
1904	*	£12	£95	£275
1905	£40	£120	£600	£1500
1906	*	*	£50	£150
1907	*	*	£60	£175
1908	£8	£20	£125	£275
1909	£8	£20	£135	£300
1910	*	*	£45	£100

GEORGE V

	F	VF	EF	Unc
1911	*	*	£18	£40
1911 proof	*	*		
1912	*	*	£25	£65
1913	*	*	£40	£80
1914	*	*	£15	£35
1915	*	*	£15	£35
1916	*	*	£15	£35
1917	*	*	£17	£35
1918	*	*	£15	£30
1919	*	*	£20	£45
1920	*	*	£20	£40
1921	*	*	£25	£50

George V nickel trial shilling, 1924

	F	VF	EF	Unc
1922	*	*	£22	£45
1923	*	*	£18	£40
1923 nickel	*	*	£600	£900
1924	*	*	£25	£45
1924 nickel	*	*	£600	£900
1925	*	*	£30	£80
1926	*	*	£18	£60
1926 mod eff	*	*	£18	£45
1927 –	*	*	£18	£45
1927 new type	*	*	£8	£35
1927 – proof	*	*	*	£35
1928	*	*	*	£18
1929	*	*	£7	£20
1930	*	*	£15	£40
1931	*	*	£7	£20
1932	*	*	£7	£20
1933	*	*	£7	£20
1934	*	*	£10	£35
1935	*	*	£3	£15
1936	*	*	£3	£15

GEORGE VI

	F	VF	EF	Unc
1937 Eng	*	*	*	£7
1937 Eng prf	*	*	*	£12
1937 Scot	*	*	*	£7
1937 Scot prf	*	*	*	£12
1938 Eng	*	*	£5	£22
1938 Scot	*	*	£5	£20
1939 Eng	*	*	*	£10
1939 Scot	*	*	*	£10
1940 Eng	*	*	*	£10
1940 Scot	*	*	*	£10
1941 Eng	*	*	*	£10
1941 Scot	*	*	£2	£10
1942 Eng	*	*	*	£10
1942 Scot	*	*	*	£10
1943 Eng	*	*	*	£10
1943 Scot	*	*	*	£10
1944 Eng	*	*	*	£7
1944 Scot	*	*	*	£8
1945 Eng	*	*	*	£8
1945 Scot	*	*	*	£7
1946 Eng	*	*	*	£7
1946 Scot	*	*	*	£7
1947 Eng	*	*	*	£6
1947 Scot	*	*	*	£6

Reverses: English (left), Scottish (right)

	F	VF	EF	Unc
1948 Eng	*	*	*	£7
1948 Scot	*	*	*	£7
1949 Eng	*	*	*	£15
1949 Scot	*	*	*	£15
1950 Eng	*	*	*	£17
1950 Eng prf	*	*	*	£17
1950 Scot	*	*	*	£17
1950 Scot prf	*	*	*	£17
1951 Eng	*	*	*	£17
1951 Eng prf	*	*	*	£17
1951 Scot	*	*	*	£17
1951 Scot prf	*	*	*	£17

ELIZABETH II

	F	VF	EF	Unc
1953 Eng	*	*	*	£5
1953 Eng prf	*	*	*	£10
1953 Scot	*	*	*	£5
1953 Scot prf	*	*	*	£10
1954 Eng	*	*	*	£5
1954 Scot	*	*	*	£5
1955 Eng	*	*	*	£5
1955 Scot	*	*	*	£5
1956 Eng	*	*	*	£7
1956 Scot	*	*	*	£9
1957 Eng	*	*	*	£4
1957 Scot	*	*	*	£15
1958 Eng	*	*	*	£15
1958 Scot	*	*	*	£4

Reverses: English (left), Scottish (right)

	F	VF	EF	Unc
1959 Eng	*	*	*	£4
1959 Scot	*	*	*	£25
1960 Eng	*	*	*	£2
1960 Scot	*	*	*	£3
1961 Eng	*	*	*	£2
1961 Scot	*	*	*	£10
1962 Eng	*	*	*	£1
1962 Scot	*	*	*	£1
1963 Eng	*	*	*	£1
1963 Scot	*	*	*	£1
1964 Eng	*	*	*	£1
1964 Scot	*	*	*	£1
1965 Eng	*	*	*	£1
1965 Scot	*	*	*	£1
1966 Eng	*	*	*	£1
1966 Scot	*	*	*	£1

Sixpences

CROMWELL	F	VF	EF
1658		of the highest rarity	
1658 Dutch copy	*	£2000	£4000

CHARLES II	F	VF	EF
1674	£50	£200	£675
1675	£50	£200	£675
1675/4	£50	£200	£700
1676	£50	£200	£700
1676/5	£50	£200	£700
1677	£50	£200	£725
1678/7	£50	£200	£725

Charles II 1678 sixpence

	F	VF	EF
1679	£50	£200	£725
1680	£70	£325	£900

SIXPENCES

	F	VF	EF
1681	£50	£200	£650
1682	£65	£275	£725
1682/1	£50	£200	£650
1683	£50	£200	£600
1684	£65	£275	£700

James II 1688 sixpence

JAMES II

	F	VF	EF
1686 early shields	£100	£350	£900
1687 –	£100	£350	£900
1687/6	£100	£350	£900
1687 later shield	£100	£350	£900
1687/6	£100	£375	£1000
1688 –	£100	£375	£1000

WILLIAM AND MARY

	F	VF	EF
1693	£110	£375	£900
1693 3 upside down	£125	£400	£900
1694	£140	£400	£1000

William and Mary 1694 sixpence

WILLIAM III

	F	VF	EF
1695 1st bust early harp	£40	£100	£450
1696 - -	£30	£80	£250
1696 - - no obv stops	£35	£100	£375
1696/5	£35	£110	£375
1696 - - B	£30	£80	£350
1696 - - C	£35	£100	£400
1696 - - E	£35	£100	£400
1696 - - N	£35	£100	£400
1696 - - y	£30	£95	£375
1696 - - Y	£40	£100	£385
1696 - later harp	£50	£135	£350
1696 - - B	£50	£175	£450
1696 - - C	£60	£225	£475
1696 - - N	£60	£185	£475
1696 2nd bust	£175	£485	£1200
1696 - - E, 3rd Bust, early harp		Extremely rare	
1696 - - y, 3rd Bust, early harp		Extremely rare	
1697 1st bust early harp	£25	£60	£250
1697 - - B	£40	£100	£350
1697 - - C	£40	£110	£350
1697 - - E	£40	£110	£350
1697 - - N	£40	£95	£350
1697 - - y	£40	£95	£350
1697 2nd bust	£125	£375	£1000
1697 3rd bust later harp	£25	£75	£250
1697 - - B	£40	£100	£350
1697 - - C	£60	£125	£425
1697 - - E	£65	£120	£425
1697 - - Y	£55	£120	£425
1698 - -	£45	£110	£300
1698 - - plumes	£95	£225	£475
1699 - -	£85	£250	£525
1699 - - plumes	£100	£225	£500

William III 1699 sixpence, plumes

	F	VF	EF
1699 - - roses	£100	£225	£600
1700	£30	£80	£225
1700 plume below bust	£2500	*	*
1701	£30	£80	£250
ANNE			
1703 VIGO	£40	£110	£300
1705	£60	£185	£525
1705 plumes	£50	£150	£400
1705 roses & plumes	£45	£150	£425
1707 –	£40	£140	£375
1707 plain	£25	£75	£200
1707 E	£20	£100	£300

Anne 1707 sixpence, E below bust

	F	VF	EF
1707 plumes	£35	£95	£300
1708 plain	£30	£95	£250
1708 E	£35	£80	£325
1708/7 E	£60	£135	£400
1708 E★	£40	£110	£350
1708/7 E★	£60	£135	£375
1708 Edin bust E★	£45	£110	£375
1708 plumes	£45	£125	£350
1710 roses & plumes	£45	£125	£350
1711	£18	£75	£195

George I 1717 sixpence

GEORGE I

	F	VF	EF
1717	£50	£175	£475
1720/17	£50	£175	£475
1723 SS C, Small letters on obv	£25	£85	£250
1723 SS C, large letters on both sides	£25	£85	£250
1726 roses & plumes	£35	£200	£475

GEORGE II

	F	VF	EF
1728 YH	£65	£225	£525
1728 – plumes	£45	£150	£400
1728 – r & p	£25	£110	£325
1731 - -	£25	£110	£325
1732 - -	£25	£110	£325
1734 - -	£35	£125	£400
1735 - -	£35	£125	£400
1736 - -	£30	£125	£375
1739 – roses	£25	£100	£325
1739 – – O/R	£60	£185	£450

	F	VF	EF
1741 – –	£25	£110	£300
1743 OH	£25	£110	£300
1745 – –	£25	£110	£300
1745/3 – –	£30	£125	£375
1745 – LIMA	£20	£85	£185
1746 – LIMA	£20	£85	£185
1746 – plain proof	*	*	£750

George II 1746 sixpence

	F	VF	EF
1750	£35	£135	£350
1751	£35	£175	£425
1757	£8	£20	£50
1757	£8	£20	£50
1758/7	£10	£35	£60

GEORGE III

	F	VF	EF	Unc
1787 hearts	£10	£20	£50	£85
1787 no hearts	£10	£20	£50	£85
1816	£8	£12	£35	£85
1817	£8	£12	£35	£85
1818	£8	£18	£45	£120
1819	£8	£15	£40	£95
1819 small 8	£10	£20	£85	£175
1820	£8	£15	£40	£100
1820 1 inverted	£30	£100	£350	£600

GEORGE IV

	F	VF	EF	Unc
1820 1st hd 1st rev ...	*	*	*	£2,500
(pattern or proof)				
1821 1st hd 1st rev ...	£8	£20	£125	£275
1821 – –				
BBITANNIAR	£100	£250	£600	*
1824 1st hd 2nd				
rev	£8	£20	£120	£250
1825 – –	£8	£20	£120	£250
1826 – –	£20	£60	£225	£525
1826 2nd hd 3rd				
rev	£5	£14	£85	£250

George IV 1825 sixpence

	F	VF	EF	Unc
1826 – – proof	*	*	*	£250
1827	£15	£45	£200	£500
1828	£8	£20	£125	£325
1829	£6	£20	£110	£275

WILLIAM IV

	F	VF	EF	Unc
1831	£6	£20	£110	£250
1831 proof	*	*	*	£300
1834	£6	£30	£120	£250
1835	£6	£20	£120	£250
1836	£15	£35	£175	£325
1837	£12	£30	£175	£325

VICTORIA

	F	VF	EF	Unc
1838	£5	£12	£85	£175
1839	£5	£12	£85	£175
1839 proof	*	*	*	£350

SIXPENCES

	F	VF	EF	Unc
1840	£5	£10	£85	£175
1841	£5	£10	£85	£215
1842	£5	£10	£85	£175
1843	£5	£10	£85	£175
1844	£5	£10	£85	£175
1845	£5	£10	£85	£175
1846	£3	£10	£85	£175
1848	£15	£90	£400	£700
1848/6	£10	£80	£325	£725
1848/7	£10	£80	£350	£750
1850	£5	£18	£90	£200
1850 5 over 3	£15	£45	£250	£450
1851	£4	£12	£85	£185
1852	£4	£12	£85	£165
1853	£5	£15	£85	£145
1853 proof	*	*	*	£400
1854	£40	£125	£600	*
1855	£4	£12	£85	£175
1856	£4	£12	£85	£185
1857	£4	£12	£85	£185
1858	£4	£12	£85	£175
1859	£4	£12	£85	£175
1859/8	£8	£20	£85	£185
1860	£5	£15	£85	£185
1862	£20	£60	£350	£750
1863	£12	£40	£250	£675
1864	£5	£12	£75	£135
1865	£6	£14	£85	£210
1866	£5	£12	£75	£175
1866 no die no. ...	*	*	*	*
1867	£8	£20	£85	£200
1868	£8	£20	£85	£200
1869	£8	£25	£120	£250
1870	£8	£20	£120	£250
1871	£5	£12	£65	£185
1871 no die no. ...	£5	£12	£65	£185
1872	£5	£12	£65	£175
1873	£5	£12	£65	£175
1874	£5	£12	£65	£175
1875	£5	£12	£70	£175
1876	£6	£20	£90	£225
1877	£5	£12	£65	£150
1877 no die no. ...	£5	£12	£65	£150
1878	£5	£10	£60	£150
1878 DRITANNIAR...	£65	£150	£600	*
1879 die no.	£8	£20	£85	£225
1879 no die no. ...	£5	£10	£60	£150
1880 2nd YH	£7	£15	£60	£150
1880 3rd YH	£3	£8	£40	£100
1881	£4	£10	£40	£95
1882	£8	£20	£75	£195
1883	£4	£10	£35	£90
1884	£4	£10	£35	£90
1885	£4	£10	£35	£80
1886	£4	£10	£35	£90
1887 YH	£4	£10	£35	£90
1887 JH shield rev	£2	£5	£10	£28

1887 Jubilee Head sixpence, withdrawn type

	F	VF	EF	Unc
1887 – proof	*	*	*	£90
1887 – new rev	£2	£5	£10	£30
1888	£3	£5	£20	£55
1889	£3	£7	£20	£55

SIXPENCES

	F	VF	EF	Unc
1890	*	£3	£20	£55
1891	*	£3	£23	£60
1892	*	£3	£23	£60
1893	£250	£650	£1950	*
1893 OH	*	£3	£15	£45
1893 proof	*	*	*	£100
1894	*	£3	£25	£45
1895	*	£3	£25	£45
1896	*	£3	£25	£45
1897	*	£3	£20	£40
1898	*	£3	£20	£40
1899	*	£3	£25	£45
1900	*	£3	£20	£40
1901	*	£3	£20	£40

EDWARD VII
	F	VF	EF	Unc
1902	*	£5	£25	£45
1902 matt proof ...	*	*	*	£40
1903	*	£7	£25	£75
1904	*	£12	£45	£110
1905	*	£8	£30	£90
1906	*	£5	£25	£80
1907	*	£7	£25	£80
1908	*	£8	£35	£95
1909	*	£6	£30	£80
1910	*	£6	£22	£50

GEORGE V
	F	VF	EF	Unc
1911	*	*	£12	£35
1911 proof	*	*	*	£45
1912	*	*	£20	£50
1913	*	*	£30	£50
1914	*	*	£12	£30
1915	*	*	£12	£30
1916	*	*	£12	£30
1917	*	*	£25	£60
1918	*	*	£12	£28
1919	*	*	£12	£35
1920	*	*	£12	£40
1920 debased	*	*	£12	£40
1921	*	*	£10	£30
1922	*	*	£10	£30
1923	*	*	£10	£40
1924	*	*	£10	£35
1925	*	*	£10	£30
1925 new rim	*	*	£12	£25
1926 new rim	*	*	£12	£30
1926 mod effigy ...	*	*	£7	£25
1927	*	*	£5	£25
1927 new rev prf ...	*	*	£5	£30
1928	*	*	£5	£17
1929	*	*	£5	£17
1930	*	*	£5	£17
1931	*	*	£5	£17
1932	*	*	£8	£22
1933	*	*	£5	£15
1934	*	*	£6	£20

George V 1929 sixpence

	F	VF	EF	Unc
1935	*	*	£5	£15
1936	*	*	£5	£15

GEORGE VI
	F	VF	EF	Unc
1937	*	*	£1	£7
1937 proof	*	*	*	£10
1938	*	*	£4	£12
1939	*	*	£2	£8
1940	*	*	£2	£8
1941	*	*	£2	£8
1942	*	*	£1	£7
1943	*	*	£1	£7
1944	*	*	£1	£7
1945	*	*	£1	£7
1946	*	*	£1	£7
1947	*	*	*	£7
1948	*	*	£1	£5
1949	*	*	£1	£8
1950	*	*	£1	£8
1950 proof	*	*	*	£10
1951	*	*	£1	£12
1951 proof	*	*	*	£10
1952	*	£5	£20	£50

ELIZABETH II
	F	VF	EF	Unc
1953	*	*	*	£3
1953 proof	*	*	*	£5
1954	*	*	*	£5
1955	*	*	*	£3
1956	*	*	*	£3
1957	*	*	*	£3
1958	*	*	*	£2
1959	*	*	*	£2
1960	*	*	*	£2
1961	*	*	*	£2
1962	*	*	*	£1
1963	*	*	*	£1
1964	*	*	*	£1
1965	*	*	*	£1
1966	*	*	*	£1
1967	*	*	*	£1

Groats (fourpences)

William IV 1836 groat
Earlier dates are included in Maundy sets

WILLIAM IV
	F	VF	EF	Unc
1836	*	*	£45	£85
1836 proof	*	*	*	£575
1837	*	*	£60	£110

Victoria 1842 groat

VICTORIA
	F	VF	EF	Unc
1838	*	£5	£25	£80
1838 8 over 8 on side	*	£10	£40	£125
1839	*	£8	£30	£85
1839 proof	*	*	*	£275
1840	£2	£10	£35	£90
1840 narrow 0	*	£12	£60	*
1841	£3	£10	£40	£95
1841 I for last 1	*	*	*	*
1842	*	£8	£35	£95

	F	VF	EF	Unc
1842/1	£4	£15	£70	£135
1843	*	£5	£40	£95
1844	*	£8	£40	£95
1845	*	£8	£40	£95
1846	*	£8	£40	£95
1847/6	£25	£70	£325	*
1848	*	£8	£35	£80
1848/6	£25	£80	£325	*
1848/7	£5	£20	£70	£200
1849	*	£10	£35	£85
1849/8	*	£10	£50	£100
1851	£15	£60	£200	*
1852	£40	£100	£300	*
1853	£35	£90	£400	*
1853 proof	*	*	*	£375
1854	*	£8	£30	£80
1854 5 over 3	£5	£20	£60	*
1855	*	£8	£25	£80
1857 proof	*	*	*	£950
1862 proof	*	*	*	£1500
1888 JH	£5	£20	£40	£80

Silver threepences

Earlier dates are included in Maundy sets

WILLIAM IV	F	VF	EF	Unc
1834	*	£10	£60	£150
1835	*	£10	£60	£135
1836	*	£10	£60	£150
1837	£10	£20	£75	£175

Victoria threepence of 1848

VICTORIA		VF	EF	Unc
1838	*	£8	£70	£125
1839	*	£10	£100	£175
1840	*	£10	£100	£150
1841	*	£10	£100	£175
1842	*	£10	£100	£175
1843	*	£10	£90	£145
1844	*	£12	£100	£175
1845	*	£5	£45	£100
1846	*	£15	£110	£185
1847	*	*	£400	£800
1848	*	*	£400	£750
1849	*	£12	£100	£175
1850	*	£5	£50	£100
1851	*	£8	£50	£135
1852	£45	£175	£450	*
1853	*	£20	£100	£200
1854	*	£8	£60	£100
1855	*	£12	£100	£175
1856	*	£10	£95	£165
1857	*	£10	£90	£175
1858	*	£8	£50	£125
1858/6	*	£25	£150	*
1859	*	£4	£50	£125
1860	*	£8	£50	£175
1861	*	£4	£60	£110
1862	*	£8	£65	£110
1863	*	£10	£90	£145
1864	*	£8	£65	£125
1865	*	£10	£70	£150
1866	*	£8	£60	£125
1867	*	£8	£60	£125

SILVER THREEPENCES

	F	VF	EF	Unc
1868	*	£8	£65	£120
1868 RRITANNIAR	ext.rare			*
1869	£10	£30	£110	£185
1870	*	£6	£50	£85
1871	*	£7	£60	£100
1872	*	£5	£55	£100
1873	*	£5	£35	£75
1874	*	£5	£35	£65
1875	*	£5	£35	£65
1876	*	£5	£35	£65
1877	*	£5	£35	£65
1878	*	£5	£35	£65
1879	*	£5	£35	£65
1880	*	£6	£40	£70
1881	*	£6	£40	£70
1882	*	£8	£45	£100
1883	*	£5	£30	£60
1884	*	£5	£30	£55
1885	*	£5	£25	£55
1886	*	£5	£25	£50
1887 YH	*	£6	£30	£55
1887 JH	*	£2	£5	£15
1887 proof	*	*	*	£40
1888	*	£2	£7	£30
1889	*	£2	£6	£25
1890	*	£2	£6	£25
1891	*	£2	£6	£25
1892	*	£3	£10	£30
1893	£12	£40	£100	£275
1893 OH	*	*	£4	£20
1893 OH proof	*	*	*	£65
1894	*	£2	£8	£25
1895	*	£2	£8	£25
1896	*	£2	£6	£25
1897	*	*	£5	£25
1898	*	*	£5	£25
1899	*	*	£5	£25
1900	*	*	£5	£25
1901	*	*	£5	£20

EDWARD VII			EF	Unc
1902	*	*	£6	£12
1902 matt proof	*	*	*	£15
1903	*	£1.50	£15	£40
1904	*	£6	£25	£65
1905	*	£6	£25	£40
1906	*	£3	£20	£40
1907	*	£1.50	£15	£40
1908	*	£1.50	£12	£35
1909	*	£2	£25	£50
1910	*	£1.25	£10	£25

George V 1927 threepence, acorns on reverse

GEORGE V			EF	Unc
1911	*	*	£4	£17
1911 proof	*	*	*	£30
1912	*	*	£4	£17
1913	*	*	£4	£17
1914	*	*	£3	£15
1915	*	*	£3	£15
1916	*	*	£2	£12
1917	*	*	£2	£12
1918	*	*	£3	£12
1919	*	*	£3	£12

SILVER THREEPENCES

	F	VF	EF	Unc
1920	*	*	£2	£17
1920 debased	*	*	£2	£17
1921	*	*	£2	£20
1922	*	*	£2	£20
1925	*	£1	£6	£28
1926	*	£3	£10	£32
1926 mod effigy ...	*	£1	£6	£28
1927 new rev prf ...	*	*	*	£45
1928	*	£2	£6	£35
1930	*	£1.50	£5	£15
1931	*	*	£1	£7
1932	*	*	£1	£7
1933	*	*	£1	£7
1934	*	*	£1	£7
1935	*	*	£1	£7
1936	*	*	£1	£7

GEORGE VI

	F	VF	EF	Unc
1937	*	*	£1	£2
1937 proof	*	*	*	£10
1938	*	*	£1	£6
1939	*	£1	£3	£10
1940	*	*	£1	£8
1941	*	*	£1	£12
1942	£1	£2	£6	£35
1943	£1	£3	£17	£55
1944	£1.50	£5	£28	£80
1945[2]	*	*	*	*

[1]Threepences issued for use in the Colonies.
[2]All specimens of 1945 were thought to have been melted down but it appears that one or two still exist.

Small silver for Colonies

These tiny coins were struck for use in some of the Colonies – they were never issued for circulation in Britain. However, they are often included in collections of British coins and it is for this reason that prices for them are given here.

TWOPENCES

Other dates are included in Maundy sets.

VICTORIA	F	VF	EF	Unc
1838	*	£2	£20	£45
1838 2nd 8 like S ...	*	£6	£30	£75
1848	*	£2	£20	£50

THREEHALFPENCES

WILLIAM IV	F	VF	EF	Unc
1834	*	£5	£40	£75
1835	*	£5	£65	£165
1835/4	*	£10	£40	£95
1836	*	£5	£35	£60
1837	£10	£25	£100	£265

VICTORIA	F	VF	EF	Unc
1838	*	£5	£25	£65
1839	*	£3	£25	£65
1840	*	£7	£65	£135
1841	*	£5	£30	£80
1842	*	£5	£30	£80
1843	*	£5	£15	£50

George V threepence

	F	VF	EF	Unc
1843/34	£5	£20	£65	£150
1860	£4	£15	£45	£110
1862	£4	£15	£45	£110
1870 proof			Extremely rare	

Maundy sets

EF prices are for evenly matched sets

Charles II 1677 Maundy set

CHARLES II	F	VF	EF
1670	£100	£200	£450
1671	£100	£200	£450
1672	£100	£200	£475
1673	£100	£200	£450
1674	£100	£200	£450
1675	£100	£225	£475
1676	£100	£225	£475
1677	£100	£200	£450
1678	£100	£250	£500
1679	£100	£225	£475
1680	£100	£200	£450
1681	£100	£250	£500
1682	£100	£225	£475
1683	£100	£200	£450
1684	£100	£225	£475

JAMES II	F	VF	EF
1686	£100	£295	£600
1687	£100	£295	£600
1688	£100	£295	£600

WILLIAM AND MARY	F	VF	EF
1689	£300	£550	£1200
1691	£125	£275	£700
1692	£135	£275	£750
1693	£135	£275	£750
1694	£125	£250	£650

WILLIAM III	F	VF	EF
1698	£100	£250	£600
1699	£100	£275	£625
1700	£100	£275	£625
1701	£100	£250	£600

114

	F	VF	EF
ANNE			
1703	£100	£165	£550
1705	£100	£165	£550
1706	£100	£150	£500
1708	£100	£175	£550
1709	£100	£165	£500
1710	£100	£175	£550
1713	£100	£150	£550
GEORGE I			
1723	£100	£185	£550
1727	£100	£150	£525
GEORGE II			
1729	£90	£150	£400
1731	£90	£150	£400
1732	£90	£150	£350
1735	£90	£150	£350
1737	£90	£150	£350
1739	£90	£150	£350
1740	£90	£150	£350
1743	£90	£150	£400
1746	£90	£150	£325
1760	£90	£195	£375

GEORGE III	F	VF	EF	Unc
1763	*	£75	£175	£300
1766	*	£80	£200	£300
1772	*	£20	£200	£300
1780	*	£80	£200	£300
1784	*	£80	£200	£300
1786	*	£80	£200	£300
1792 wire type	*	£125	£350	£500

William and Mary 1694 Maundy set

	F	VF	EF	Unc
1795	*	£60	£125	£275
1800	*	£60	£125	£275
1817	*	£65	£125	£275
1818	*	£65	£125	£275
1820	*	£65	£125	£275
GEORGE IV				
1822	*	*	£100	£225
1823	*	*	£100	£225
1824	*	*	£100	£225
1825	*	*	£100	£225
1826	*	*	£100	£225
1827	*	*	£100	£225
1828	*	*	£100	£225
1829	*	*	£100	£225
1830	*	*	£100	£225
WILLIAM IV				
1831	*	*	£110	£850
1831 proof	*	*	*	£400
1832	*	*	£110	£285
1833	*	*	£100	£250
1834	*	*	£100	£250
1835	*	*	£100	£250

MAUNDY SETS

	F	VF	EF	Unc
1836	*	*	£120	£300
1837	*	*	£120	£300
VICTORIA				
1838			£80	£165
1839			£85	£165
1839 proof			*	£375
1840			£85	£175
1841			£85	£200
1842			£90	£185
1843			£90	£180
1844			£90	£180
1845			£80	£175
1846			£95	£200
1847			£90	£195

George IV 1825

			EF	Unc
1848			£85	£160
1849			£95	£200
1850			£75	£140
1851			£75	£140
1852			£80	£160
1853			£80	£160
1853 proof			*	£500
1854			£80	£175
1855			£80	£175
1856			£80	£150
1857			£80	£150
1858			£80	£150
1859			£80	£150
1860			£80	£135
1861			£80	£125
1862			£80	£125
1863			£80	£125
1864			£80	£125
1865			£80	£125
1866			£80	£125
1867			£80	£125
1868			£80	£125
1869			£80	£125
1870			£80	£125
1871			£80	£125
1872			£80	£125
1873			£80	£125
1874			£80	£125
1875			£80	£125
1876			£80	£125
1877			£80	£125
1878			£80	£125
1879			£80	£125
1880			£80	£125
1881			£80	£125
1882			£80	£125
1883			£80	£125
1884			£80	£125
1885			£80	£125
1886			£80	£125
1887			£80	£125
1888 JH			£60	£100

MAUNDY SETS

	EF	Unc
1889	£70	£120
1890	£70	£120
1891	£70	£120
1892	£70	£120
1893 OH	£60	£80
1894	£60	£80
1895	£60	£80
1896	£60	£80
1897	£60	£80
1898	£60	£80
1899	£60	£80
1900	£60	£95
1901	£60	£80

EDWARD VII

	EF	Unc
1902	£55	£80
1902 matt proof	*	£75
1903	£55	£75
1904	£55	£75
1905	£55	£75
1906	£55	£75
1907	£55	£75
1908	£55	£75
1909	£70	£110
1910	£70	£110

GEORGE V

	EF	Unc
1911	£50	£90
1911 proof	*	£100
1912	£50	£90
1913	£50	£90
1914	£50	£90
1915	£50	£90
1916	£50	£90
1917	£50	£90
1918	£50	£90
1919	£50	£90
1920	£50	£90
1921	£50	£90
1922	£50	£90
1923	£50	£90
1924	£50	£90
1925	£50	£90
1926	£50	£90
1927	£50	£90
1928	£50	£90
1929	£50	£90
1930	£50	£90
1931	£50	£90
1932	£50	£90
1933	£50	£90
1934	£50	£90
1935	£50	£90
1936	£55	£90

GEORGE VI

	EF	Unc
1937	*	£75
1938	*	£80
1939	*	£80
1940	*	£80
1941	*	£80
1942	*	£80
1943	*	£80
1944	*	£80
1945	*	£80
1946	*	£80
1947	*	£80
1948	*	£80
1949	*	£80
1950	*	£80
1951	*	£80
1952	*	£80

ELIZABETH II

	EF	Unc
1953	£200	£450
1954	*	£100
1955	*	£100
1956	*	£100
1957	*	£100
1958	*	£100
1959	*	£100
1960	*	£100
1961	*	£100
1962	*	£100
1963	*	£100
1964	*	£100
1965	*	£100
1966	*	£100
1967	*	£100
1968	*	£100
1969	*	£100
1970	*	£90
1971	*	£90
1972	*	£90
1973	*	£90
1974	*	£90
1975	*	£90
1976	*	£90
1977	*	£90
1978	*	£90
1979	*	£90
1980	*	£90
1981	*	£90
1982	*	£90
1983	*	£90
1984	*	£90
1985	*	£90
1986	*	£90
1987	*	£90
1988	*	£90
1989	*	£90
1990	*	£90
1991	*	£90
1992	*	£90
1993	*	£90
1994	*	£90
1995	*	£90
1996	*	£90
1997	*	£90
1998	*	£90
1999	*	£95
2000	*	£95
2001	*	£100
2002	*	£110
2002 gold (from set)	*	£950
2003	*	£125
2004	*	£135
2005	*	£150

1925 Maundy (part set)

Nickel-brass threepences

1937 threepence of Edward VII, extremely rare

1937-dated Edward VIII threepences, struck in 1936 ready for issue, were melted after Edward's abdication. A few, however, escaped into circulation to become highly prized collectors' pieces. George VI 1937 threepences were struck in large numbers.

EDWARD VIII	F	VF	EF	BU
1937	*	*	£25000	*

GEORGE VI				
1937	*	*	£1	£4
1938	*	*	£3	£20
1939	*	*	£6	£40
1940	*	*	£2	£15
1941	*	*	£1	£8
1942	*	*	£1	£8
1943	*	*	£1	£8
1944	*	*	£1	£8
1945	*	*	£1	£8
1946	£2	£10	£100	£375
1948	*	*	£5	£20
1949	£2	£10	£100	£325
1950	*	*	£10	£40
1951	*	*	£10	£60
1952	*	*	*	£12

Elizabeth II 1953 nickel-brass threepence

ELIZABETH II				
1953	*	*	*	£3
1953 proof	*	*	*	£8
1954	*	*	*	£5
1955	*	*	*	£7
1956	*	*	£1	£7
1957	*	*	*	£4
1958	*	*	£2	£7
1959	*	*	*	£3
1960	*	*	*	£3
1961	*	*	*	£1
1962	*	*	*	£1
1963	*	*	*	£1
1964	*	*	*	£1
1965	*	*	*	£1
1966	*	*	*	*
1967	*	*	*	*

Copper twopence

George III 1797 'cartwheel' twopence

GEORGE III	F	VF	EF	BU
1797	£20	£75	£350	*

Copper pennies

GEORGE III	F	VF	EF	BU
1797 10 leaves	£5	£35	£225	*
1797 11 leaves	£8	£45	£225	*

1797 'cartwheel' penny

	F	VF	EF	BU
1806	£3	£8	£90	£300
1806 no incuse curl	£3	£8	£90	£300
1807	£3	£8	£90	£300

1806 penny of George III

GEORGE IV	F	VF	EF	BU
1825	£5	£15	£150	£400
1826	£3	£12	£150	£400
1826 thin line down St Andrew's cross	£5	£15	£150	£400
1826 thick line	£5	£15	£150	£400
1827	£200	£550		£2000

COPPER PENNIES

William IV 1831 penny

WILLIAM IV

	F	VF	EF	BU
1831	£10	£50	£250	*
1831.w.w incuse ...	£12	£60	£300	*
1831.w.w incuse ...	£15	£75	£350	*
1834	£15	£75	£300	*
1837	£20	£100	£600	*

Victoria 1841 copper penny

VICTORIA

	F	VF	EF	Unc
1839 proof	*	*	*	£750
1841	£12	£30	£75	£325
1841 no colon after REG	£3	£15	£85	£350
1843	£45	£200	£900	£2500
1843 no colon after REG	£30	£125	£800	£2250
1844	£3	£15	£70	£225
1845	£8	£20	£95	£300
1846 DEF far colon	£3	£15	£80	£275
1846 DEF close colon	£3	£15	£90	£325
1847 DEF close colon	£3	£15	£60	£200
1847 DEF far colon	£3	£15	£60	£200

	F	VF	EF	BU
1848	£3	£15	£60	£200
1848/6	£15	£35	£250	*
1848/7	£3	£15	£60	£200
1849	£40	£120	£800	*
1851 DEF far colon	£3	£15	£100	£325
1851 DEF close colon	£4	£15	£100	£275
1853 OT	£2	£10	£50	£165
1853 colon nearer F	£3	£10	£60	£200
1853 PT	£2	£10	£60	£200
1854 PT	£2	£10	£60	£165
1854/3	£15	£50	£100	£250
1854 OT	£2	£10	£60	£165
1855 OT	£2	£10	£60	£165
1855 PT	£2	£10	£60	£165
1856 PT	£50	£200	£425	*
1856 OT	£20	£50	£275	£1000
1857 OT	£2	£10	£60	£165
1857 PT	£2	£10	£60	£165
1857 small date ...	£2	£10	£75	£225
1858	£2	£10	£60	£165
1858 small date ...	£3	£10	£65	£200
1858/3 now thought to be 1858 9/8 (see below)				
1858/7	£2	£5	£55	£190
1858/6	£15	£35	£100	*
1858 no ww	£2	£5	£85	£175
1858 no ww (large 1 and 5 small 8s)	£3	£8	£60	£185
1858 9/8?	£12	£25	£70	£200
1858 9/8? large rose	£12	£30	£80	£225
1859	£3	£10	£55	£175
1859 small date ...	£4	£15	£60	£175
1860/59	£300	£700	£1900	*

Bronze pennies

For fuller details of varieties in bronze pennies see English Copper, Tin and Bronze Coins in the British Museum 1558-1958 by C. W. Peck; The Bronze Coinage of Great Britain by M. J. Freeman and The British Bronze Penny 1860-1970 by Michael Gouby.

VICTORIA

	F	VF	EF	BU
1860 RB, shield crossed with incuse treble lines	*	£15	£55	£225
1860 RB, shield crossed raised lines	£8	£20	£65	£250
1860 RB, double lines, but farther apart, rock to left of lighthouse	£20	£100	£500	£1000
1860 RB obv/TB rev	£150	£450	£2250	*
1860 TB obv/RB rev	£150	£450	£2250	*

1860 penny, toothed border on obverse

	F	VF	EF	BU
1860 TB, L.C. WYON on truncation, L.C.W. incuse below shield	*	£17	£60	£225

	F	VF	EF	BU
1860 TB, same obv but L.C.W. incuse below foot … … …	£60	£175	£550	£1200
1860 TB, as previous but heavy flan of 170 grains … … …		ext. rare		
1860 TB, LC, WYON below truncation, L.C.W. incuse below shield … …	*	£17	£80	£265
1860 TB, no signature on obv. L.C.W. incuse below shield … …	*	£25	£80	£265
1861 L.C. WYON on truncation, L.C.W. incuse below shield	£15	£60	£280	£625
1861 same obv. no signature on rev	*	£15	£75	£285
1861 L.C. WYON below truncation, L.C.W. incuse below shield	*	£10	£70	£250
1861 similar, but heavy flan (170 grains) … … …	*	*	*	£1500
1861 same obv but no signature on rev … … … …	*	£15	£70	£275
1861 no signature on obv, L.C.W. incuse below shield … … .,	*	£15	£80	£300
1861-6/8 … … … …		ext.rare		
1861 no signature either side … … …	*	£12	£65	£225
1862 … … … … …	*	£10	£60	£225
1862 sm date figs …		ext. rare		
1863 … … … … …	*	£10	£70	£225
1863 slender 3 … …		ext. rare		
1863 die no. (2, 3 or 4) below date … … … …		ext. rare		
1864 plain 4 … … …	£80	£300	£800	£1500
1864 crossiet 4 … … …	£80	£300	£1000	£1750
1865 … … … … …	*	£25	£120	£400
1865/3 … … … … …	£40	£125	£600	£1100
1866 … … … … …	*	£15	£100	£250
1867 … … … … …	*	£30	£125	£425
1868 … … … … …	£6	£40	£125	£600
1869 … … … … …	£50	£200	£1500	£2500
1870 … … … … …	£6	£40	£175	£425
1871 … … … … …	£10	£70	£400	£875
1872 … … … … …	*	£12	£75	£250
1873 … … … … …	*	£12	£75	£250
1874 (1873 type) …	*	£12	£75	£250
1874 H (1873 type)	*	£12	£80	£265
1874 new rev, lighthouse tall and thin … … … … …	*	£20	£80	£250
1874 H as previous	£4	£15	£75	£275
1874 new obv/1873 rev	*	£15	£70	£250
1874 H as previous	*	£15	£70	£250
1874 new obv/new rev	*	£15	£70	£250
1874 H as previous	*	£15	£70	£250
1875 … … … … …	*	£15	£70	£250
1875 H … … … … …	£30	£200	£800	*
1876 H … … … … …	*	£15	£85	£275
1877 … … … … …	*	£8	£65	£225
1878 … … … … …	*	£15	£75	£400
1879 … … … … …	*	*	£50	£175
1880 … … … … …	*	*	£70	£275
1881 (1880 obv) … … …	*	*	£70	£275
1881 new obv … … …	*	£15	£80	£375
1881 H … … … … …	*	*	£55	£250
1882 H … … … … …	*	*	£45	£175
1882 no H … … … … …	£75	£300	*	*
1883 … … … … …	*	*	£35	£175
1884 … … … … …	*	*	£35	£150
1885 … … … … …	*	*	£35	£150
1886 … … … … …	*	*	£35	£150
1887 … … … … …	*	*	£35	£150

BRONZE PENNIES

	F	VF	EF	BU
1888 … … … … …	*	*	£30	£150
1889 14 leaves … …	*	*	£30	£150
1889 15 leaves … …	*	*	£30	£150
1890 … … … … …	*	*	£30	£150
1891 … … … … …	*	*	£30	£130
1892 … … … … …	*	*	£30	£150
1893 … … … … …	*	*	£30	£150
1894 … … … … …	*	*	£40	£200
1895 2mm … … …	*	£50	£275	£600

Victoria old head penny of 1895

	F	VF	EF	BU
1895 … … … … …	*	*	£15	£55
1896 … … … … …	*	*	£12	£50
1897 … … … … …	*	*	£12	£50
1897 higher horizon	£5	£25	£200	£500
1898 … … … … …	*	*	£15	£55
1899 … … … … …	*	*	£15	£50
1900 … … … … …	*	*	£12	£45
1901 … … … … …	*	*	£10	£25

Edward VII 1902, penny, low horizon

EDWARD VII

	F	VF	EF	BU
1902 low horizon …	*	£15	£80	£150
1902 … … … … …	*	*	£10	£35
1903 … … … … …	*	*	£20	£50
1904 … … … … …	*	*	£35	£100
1905 … … … … …	*	*	£30	£80
1906 … … … … …	*	*	£20	£65
1907 … … … … …	*	*	£20	£70

BRONZE PENNIES

	F	VF	EF	BU
1908	*	*	£17	£60
1909	*	*	£20	£60
1910	*	*	£17	£55

GEORGE V

	F	VF	EF	BU
1911	*	*	£12	£35
1912	*	*	£12	£40
1912 H	*	*	£60	£185
1913	*	*	£15	£50
1914	*	*	£12	£40
1915	*	*	£12	£40
1916	*	*	£12	£40
1917	*	*	£12	£40
1918	*	*	£12	£40
1918 H	*	£25	£200	£450
1918 KN	*	£30	£350	£750
1919	*	*	£12	£35
1919 H	*	£5	£250	£550
1919 KN	*	£10	£250	£750
1920	*	*	£12	£37
1921	*	*	£12	£37
1922	*	*	£12	£37
1922 rev as 1927 ext. rare	*	*	*	
1926	*	*	£20	£70
1926 mod effigy ...	*	£50	£800	£1650
1927	*	*	£7	£28
1928	*	*	£7	£28
1929	*	*	£7	£28
1930	*	*	£10	£28
1931	*	*	£10	£28
1932	*	*	£15	£45
1933			highest rarity	
1934	*	*	£8	£35
1935	*	*	£2	£15
1936	*	*	*	£15

GEORGE VI

	F	VF	EF	BU
1937	*	*	*	£5
1938	*	*	*	£5
1939	*	*	*	£6
1940	*	*	*	£10
1944	*	*	*	£15
1945	*	*	*	£12
1946	*	*	*	£12
1947	*	*	*	£4
1948	*	*	*	£5
1949	*	*	*	£5

George VI 1948 penny

	F	VF	EF	BU
1950	£2	£5	£17	£40
1951	£2	£5	£21	£55

ELIZABETH II

	F	VF	EF	BU
1953	*	£1	£2	£5
1953 proof	*	*	*	£5

	Fair	F	VF	EF
1961	*	*	*	£0.50
1962	*	*	*	*
1963	*	*	*	*
1964	*	*	*	*
1965	*	*	*	*
1966	*	*	*	*
1967	*	*	*	*

Copper halfpennies

All copper unless otherwise stated

Charles II 1675 halfpenny

CHARLES II

	Fair	F	VF	EF
1672	£5	£45	£150	£800
1672 CRAOLVS		Extremely rare		*
1673	£5	£45	£80	£800
1673 CRAOLVS		Extremely rare		*
1673 no stops on reverse	£10	£50	£200	£800
1673 no stops on obverse	£10	£50	£200	£800
1675	£10	£50	£200	£1250
1675 no stops on obverse	£10	£60	£200	*

James II 1685 tin halfpenny

JAMES II

	Fair	F	VF	EF
1685 (tin)	£65	£250	£550	£3000
1686 (tin)	£70	£250	£600	*
1687 (tin)	£65	£250	£550	*
1687 D over D	*	*	*	*

WILLIAM AND MARY

	Fair	F	VF	EF
1689 (tin) ET on right	£450	£900	£1500	*
1689 (tin) ET on left	*	*	*	*
1690 (tin) dated on edge	£65	£200	£500	£2500
1691 (tin) date in exergue and on edge	£65	£200	£500	£2500

	Fair	F	VF	EF
1691/2 (tin) 1691 in exergue 1692 on edge	£65	£200	£550	£2500
1692 (tin) date in exergue and on edge	£65	£75	£450	*
1694 ... ... ,...	£12	£50	£250	£1150

William and Mary 1694 halfpenny

	Fair	F	VF	EF
1694 GVLIEMVS ...	£150	*	*	*
1694 no stop after MARIA	£25	£65	£300	£1200
1694 BRITANNIA with last I over A	£30	£125	*	*
1694 no stop on reverse	£20	£60	£225	£1150

WILLIAM III
Type 1 (date in exergue)

1695	£10	£35	£175	£1100
1695 thick flan	£40	£90	£250	*
1695 BRITANNIA ...	£10	£35	£175	£1100
1695 no stop on reverse	£10	£40	£175	*
1696	£10	£35	£175	£1100
1696 GVLIEMVS, no stop on reverse ...	£40	£90	£250	*
1696 TERTVS	£30	£90	£250	*
1696 obv struck from doubled die	£25	£90	£250	*
1697	£10	£45	£120	*
1697 no stops either side	£15	£45	£175	*
1697 I of TERTIVS over E	£25	£95	£225	*
1697 GVLILMVS no stop on reverse ...	£20	£40	£185	*
1697 no stop after TERTIVS	£15	£40	£150	£1100
1698	£15	£40	£150	£1100

Type 2 (date in legend)

1698	£10	£45	£200	£1100
1699	£10	£30	£200	£950
1699 BRITANNIA ...	£10	£30	£200	£950
1699 GVLIEMVS ...	£10	£45	£200	£1200

Type 3 (Britannia's hand on knee, date in exergue)

1699	£10	£30	£200	£950
1699 stop after date	£15	£40	£225	£1000
1699 BRITANNIA ...	£10	£30	£200	£950
1699 GVILELMVS ...	£15	£40	£225	£1000
1699 TERTVS	£25	£50	£250	*
1699 no stop on reverse	£30	£60	£250	*
1699 no stops on obverse	£15	£45	£200	£1000

COPPER HALFPENNIES

	FAIR	F	VF	EF
1699 no stops after GVLIELMVS	£8	£30	£185	£950
1700	£8	£20	£185	£950
1700 no stops on obverse	£8	£20	£185	*
1700 no stop after GVLIELMVS	£8	£20	£185	*
1700 BRITANNIA ...	£8	£20	£185	£950
1700 no stops on reverse	£8	£20	£185	*
1700 GVLIELMS ...	£8	£35	£185	*
1700 GVLIEEMVS ...	£8	£35	£185	*
1700 TER TIVS	£8	£20	£185	*
1700 1 of TERTIVS over V	£8	£35	£250	*
1701 BRITANNIA ...	£8	£20	£185	*
1701 no stops on obverse	£8	£20	£185	*
1701 GVLIELMVS TERTIVS	£8	£35	£225	*

GEORGE I
Type 1

1717	£10	£30	£250	£850
1717 no stops on obverse	£15	£40	£275	£900
1718	*	£35	£250	£900
1718 no stop on obverse	£15	£40	£275	£950
1719 on larger flan of type 2	£20	£50	£325	*
1719 – edge grained	£75	£300	*	*

Type 2

1719 both shoulder straps ornate	£5	£25	£150	£725
1719 – edge grained	£10	£50	*	*
1719 bust with left strap plain	£5	£25	£150	£800
1719 – edge grained	£10	£50	*	*
1720	£5	£25	£150	£725
1721	£5	£25	£150	£725
1721/0	£5	£25	£150	*
1721 stop after date	£5	£25	£150	£725
1722	£5	£25	£150	£725
1722 GEORGIVS ...	£5	£25	£150	*
1723	£5	£25	£150	£725
1723 no stop on reverse	£5	£25	£150	£750
1724	£5	£25	£150	£650

George II 1729 halfpenny

GEORGE II
Young Head

1729	£2	£12	£80	£350
1729 no stop on reverse	£2	£12	£90	£375

COPPER HALFPENNIES

	Fair	F	VF	EF
1730	*	£12	£70	£250
1730 GEOGIVS, no stop on reverse ...	£5	£25	£110	£300
1730 stop after date	£5	£25	£85	£300
1730 no stop after REX or on reverse	£5	£25	£110	£350
1731	*	£12	£70	£250
1731 no stop on reverse	*	£25	£100	£300
1732	*	£20	£70	£250
1732 no stop on reverse	*	£25	£100	£325
1733	*	£20	£70	£250
1733 only obverse stop before REX ...	*	£20	£70	£250
1734	*	£12	£70	£250
1734/3	*	£25	£145	*
1734 no stops on obverse	*	£25	£145	*
1735	*	£18	£70	£250
1736	*	£18	£70	£250
1737	*	£18	£70	£250
1738	*	£18	£70	£250
1739	*	£18	£70	£250

Old Head

	Fair	F	VF	EF
1740	*	£7	£55	£225
1742	*	£7	£55	£225
1742/0	*	£10	£80	£225
1743	*	£7	£55	£225
1744	*	£7	£55	£225
1745	*	£7	£55	£225
1746	*	£7	£55	£225
1747	*	£7	£55	£225
1748	*	£7	£55	£225
1749	*	£7	£55	£225
1750	*	£7	£55	£225
1751	*	£7	£55	£225
1752	*	£7	£55	£225
1753	*	£7	£55	£225
1754	*	£7	£55	£225

GEORGE III

	F	VF	EF	BU
1770	£1	£40	£185	£650
1771	£1	£40	£185	£600
1771 no stop on reverse	£2	£40	£185	£600
1771 ball below spear head	£2	£40	£185	£600
1772	£2	£40	£185	£600
1772 GEORIVS	£18	£100	£275	*
1772 ball below spear head	£2	£40	£185	£600
1772 no stop on reverse	£2	£40	£185	£600
1773	£2	£40	£185	£600
1773 no stop after REX	£2	£40	£185	£600
1773 no stop on reverse	£2	£40	£185	*
1774	£2	£40	£185	£600
1775	£3	£40	£185	£650
1799 5 incuse gunports	*	£5	£50	£110
1799 6 relief gunports	*	£5	£50	£110
1799 9 relief gunports	*	*	£50	£140
1799 no gunports ...	*	*	£50	£115
1799 no gunports and raised line along hull	*	£5	£55	£150
1806 no berries on olive branch	*	*	£45	£125

	F	VF	EF	BU
1806 line under SOHO 3 berries	*	*	£45	£110
1807 similar but double-cut border bead between B and R	*	*	£45	£120

GEORGE IV

	F	VF	EF	BU
1825	*	£30	£125	£250

George IV 1826 halfpenny

	F	VF	EF	BU
1826 two incuse lines down cross	*	£15	£75	£175
1826 raised line down centre of cross ...	*	£15	£75	£200
1827	*	£12	£75	£185

WILLIAM IV

	F	VF	EF	BU
1831	*	£5	£65	£200
1834	*	£5	£65	£200
1837	*	£4	£60	£225

VICTORIA

	F	VF	EF	BU
1838	*	£3	£25	£100
1839 proof	*	*	*	£250
1839 proof, rev inv	*	*	*	£300
1841	*	£3	£25	£85
1843	£3	£30	£90	£300
1844	*	£5	£40	£100
1845	£18	£40	£450	*
1846	£2	£5	£40	£110
1847	*	£10	£40	£110
1848	*	£5	£40	£110
1848/7	*	£3	£35	£110
1851	*	£3	£25	£100
1851 7 incuse dots on and above shield	*	£3	£25	£110
1852	*	£3	£25	£100
1852 7 incuse dots on and above shield	*	£3	£25	£100
1853	*	£3	£25	£90
1853/2	£10	£25	£85	*
1854	*	£3	£15	£70

Victoria 1853 copper halfpenny

	F	VF	EF	BU
1855	*	£3	£25	£85
1856	*	£3	£35	£100
1857	*	£3	£25	£75

	F	VF	EF	BU
1857 7 incuse dots on and above shield	*	£5	£25	£85
1858	*	£5	£25	£85
1858/6	£2	£10	£35	£85
1858/7	£1	£5	£25	£70
1858 small date	£1	£5	£25	£70
1859	£1	£5	£25	£120
1859/8	£3	£10	£50	*
1860 prog	*	*	*	£6000

Bronze halfpennies

VICTORIA	F	VF	EF	BU
1860	*	£5	£30	£120
1860 TB 7 berries in wreath	*	£5	£35	£140
1860 TB4 berries in wreath	*	£5	£35	£140
1860 TB similar but centres of four of leaves are double incuse lines	*	£10	£50	£175
1861 obv 4 berries, 15 leaves, raised leaf centres rev L.C.W. on rock	*	£20	£70	£225
1861 same obv, rev no signature			ext. rare	
1861 same but lighthouse has no vertical lines	*	£15	£50	£185
1861 obv 4 berries, 4 double incuse leaf centres, rev L.C.W. on rock ...	*	£5	£45	£150
1861 same obv, rev no signature	*	£8	£45	£175
1861 obv 7 double incuse leaf centres, rev L.C.W on rock	*	£5	£45	£165
1861 same obv, rev no signature	*	£5	£40	£110
1861 obv 16 leaves, rev lighthouse has rounded top	*	£5	£40	£110
1861 same obv, rev lighthouse has pointed top	*	£5	£40	£110
1861 no signature ...	*	£5	£35	£110
1862 L.C.W. on rock	*	£5	£25	£100
1862 letter (A,B or C) left of lighthouse base ...	£75	£300	*	*
1863	*	£5	£45	£145
1864	*	£6	£45	£200
1865	*	£10	£80	£275
1865/3	£10	£50	£250	£600
1866	*	£8	£60	£200
1867	*	£8	£80	£275
1868	*	£8	£60	£225

Victoria 1889 bronze halfpenny

BRONZE HALFPENNIES

	F	VF	EF	BU
1869	*	£25	£225	£575
1870	*	£5	£55	£165
1871	£10	£45	£225	£525
1872	*	£5	£40	£145
1873	*	£7	£50	£200
1874	*	£15	£75	£300
1874H	*	£5	£40	£145
1875	*	£5	£40	£145
1875H	*	£5	£45	£145
1876H	*	£5	£40	£145
1877	*	£5	£40	£145
1878	*	£15	£60	£265
1879	*	£5	£40	£125
1880	*	£4	£40	£140
1881	*	£4	£40	£140
1881H	*	£4	£35	£140
1882H	*	£4	£35	£140
1883	*	£4	£35	£140
1884	*	£2	£30	£125
1885	*	£2	£30	£125
1886	*	*	£30	£125
1887	*	*	£30	£125
1888	*	*	£30	£125
1889	*	*	£30	£125
1889/8	*	£8	£60	£225
1890	*	*	£25	£90
1891	*	*	£25	£90
1892	*	*	£25	£90
1893	*	*	£25	£90
1894	*	£5	£35	£140
1895 OH	*	*	£3	£50
1896	*	*	£3	£30
1897 normal horizon	*	*	£3	£30
1897 higher horizon	*	*	£3	£30
1898	*	*	£6	£30
1899	*	*	£4	£30
1900	*	*	£15	£20
1901	*	*	£12	£15

EDWARD VII				
1902 low horizon ...	*	£5	£55	£110
1902	*	*	£7	£18
1903	*	*	£9	£28
1904	*	*	£11	£35
1905	*	*	£7	£25
1906	*	*	£7	£25
1907	*	*	£7	£25
1908	*	*	£7	£25
1909	*	*	£7	£30
1910	*	*	£7	£30

GEORGE V				
1911	*	*	£8	£25
1912	*	*	£8	£25

George V 1912 halfpenny

	F	VF	EF	BU
1913	*	*	£10	£35
1914	*	*	£8	£25
1915	*	*	£8	£25

BRONZE HALFPENNIES

	Fair	F	VF	EF
1916		*	£2	£25
1917	*	*	£2	£25
1918	*	*	£2	£25
1919	*	*	£2	£25
1920	*	*	£2	£25
1921	*	*	£2	£25
1922	*	*	£3	£25
1923	*	*	£2	£25
1924	*	*	£3	£25
1925	*	*	£4	£25
1925 mod effigy ...	*	*	£4	£30
1926	*	*	£4	£25
1927	*	*	£2.50	£20
1928	*	*	£2	£15
1929	*	*	£2	£15
1930	*	*	£2	£15
1931	*	*	£2	£15
1932	*	*	£2	£15
1933	*	*	£2	£15
1934	*	*	£2	£15
1935	*	*	£2	£12
1936	*	*	£2	£10

GEORGE VI

	Fair	F	VF	EF
1937	*	*	*	£4
1938	*	*	*	£6
1939	*	*	*	£8
1940	*	*	*	£9
1941	*	*	*	£5
1942	*	*	*	£4
1943	*	*	*	£4
1944	*	*	*	£5
1945	*	*	*	£4
1946	*	*	*:	£8
1947	*	*	*	£6
1948	*	*	*	£6
1949	*	*	*	£8
1950	*	*	*	£8
1951	*	*	*	£15
1952	*	*	*	£5

ELIZABETH II

	Fair	F	VF	EF
1953	*	*	*	£2
1954	*	*	*	£3
1955	*	*	*	£3
1956	*	*	*	£3
1957	*	*	*	£2
1958	*	*	*	£2
1959	*	*	*	£1
1960	*	*	*	£1
1962	*	*	*	*
1963	*	*	*	*
1964	*	*	*	*
1965	*	*	*	*
1966	*	*	*	*
1967	*	*	*	*

Copper farthings

Copper unless otherwise stated

OLIVER CROMWELL

	Fair	F	VF	EF
Patterns only	*	£2000	£5000	£6500

CHARLES II

	Fair	F	VF	EF
1671 patterns only	*	*	£350	£700
1672	£1	£30	£140	£575
1672 no stop on obverse	£2.75	£30	£140	£575
1672 loose drapery at Britannia's elbow	£2	£30	£140	£600
1673	£1	£30	£140	£600

Oliver Cromwell copper farthing

	Fair	F	VF	EF
1673 CAROLA	£30	£125	£300	*
1673 BRITANNIA ...	*	*	*	*
1673 no stops on obverse	£150	£300	*	*
1673 no stop on reverse	£50	£100	*	*
1674	*	£25	£150	£600
1675	*	£25	£150	£600
1675 no stop after CAROLVS	*	*	*	*
1676	*	£25	£150	£600
1679	*	£25	£150	£600
1679 no stop on reverse	£50	£100	£300	*
1684 (tin) various edge readings	£25	£125	£450	£2500
1685 (tin)	£30	£150	£500	*

JAMES II

	Fair	F	VF	EF
1684 (tin)		**Extremely rare**		*
1685 (tin) various edge readings	£60	£165	£600	£2500
1686 (tin) various edge readings	£70	£185	£600	£2750
1687 (tin) draped bust, various readings		**Extremely rare** *		

WILLIAM AND MARY

	Fair	F	VF	EF
1689 (tin) date in exergue and on edge, many varieties ...	£250	£500	*	*
1689/90 (tin) 1689 in exergue, 1690 on edge	*	*	*	*
1689/90 (tin) 1690 in exergue, 1689 on edge	*	*	*	*
1690 (tin) various types	£40	£150	£400	£2500
1691 (tin) small and large figures	£40	£150	£400	£2500
1692 (tin)	£40	£150	£400	£2500
1694 many varieties	£10	£50	£125	£625

WILLIAM III
Type 1, date in exergue

	Fair	F	VF	EF
1695	£40	£125		£600
1695 M over V	£60	£150	*	*
1696		£40	£125	£600
1697		£40	£125	£600

William III 1697 farthing

	Fair	F	VF	EF
1698	£25	£100	£350	*
1699	£2	£40	£125	£700
1700	£2	£40	£100	£700

	Fair	F	VF	EF
Type 2, date in legend				
1698	£5	£35	£150	£700
1699	£5	£35	£150	£700

Anne 1714 pattern farthing

ANNE

	Fair	F	VF	EF
1714 patterns (**F**) ...	*	£250	£425	£750

George I 'dump' farthing of 1717

GEORGE I
'Dump Type'

	Fair	F	VF	EF
1717	*	£100	£275	£725
1718 silver proof ...	*	*	*	£1000

Larger flan

	Fair	F	VF	EF
1719 large lettering on obverse	£3	£20	£125	£550
1719 small lettering on obverse	£3	£20	£135	£575
1719 – last A of BRITANNIA over I	£70	£200	*	*

George I 1719 farthing

	Fair	F	VF	EF
1719 legend continuous over bust	£20	£60	*	*
1720 large lettering on obverse	*	£20	£110	£500
1720 small lettering on obverse	*	£15	£110	£500
1721	*	£15	£110	£500
1721/0	£10	£30	*	*
1722 large lettering on obverse	*	£20	£110	£500
1722 small lettering on obverse	*	£20	£110	£500
1723	*	£15	£110	£525
1723 R of REX over R	£12	£30	£150	£250
1724	£5	£20	£110	£550

COPPER FARTHINGS

George II 1730 farthing

GEORGE II

	Fair	F	VF	EF
1730	*	£10	£45	£250
1731	*	£10	£45	£250
1732	*	£12	£45	£250
1733	*	£10	£40	£250
1734	*	£10	£45	£250
1734 no stops on obverse	*	£10	£60	£300
1735	*	£10	£40	£225
1735 3 over 3	*	£15	£60	£275
1736	*	£10	£40	£225
1736 triple tie-riband	*	£10	£60	£275
1737 sm date	*	£10	£40	£225
1737 lge date	*	£10	£45	£225
1739	*	£10	£40	£250
1739/5	*	*	*	*
1741 Old Head	*	£10	£45	£200
1744	*	£10	£45	£200
1746	*	£10	£45	£175
1746 V over U	*	*	*	*
1749	*	£10	£45	£175
1750	*	£10	£45	£200
1754/0	*	£20	£80	£250
1754	*	£8	£40	£125

	F	VF	EF	BU
GEORGE III				
1771	*	£20	£165	£450
1773	*	£5	£120	£400
1774	*	£5	£120	£400
1775	*	£5	£120	£400
1799	*	*	£50	£110
1806	*	£3	£50	£115
1807	*	£4	£50	£120
GEORGE IV				
1821	*	£2	£45	£100
1822	*	£2	£45	£100
1823	*	£3	£45	£100
1825	*	£3	£45	£100
1825 D of DEI over U	*	£7	£70	*
1826 date on rev ...	*	£2	£45	£120
1826 date on obv ...	*	£3	£50	£100
1826 I for 1 in date	*	*	*	*
1827	*	£3	£50	£100
1828	*	£3	£55	£120
1829	*	£5	£55	£145
1830	*	£7	£50	£120
WILLIAM IV				
1831	*	£6	£55	£135
1834	*	£6	£55	£135
1835	*	£6	£50	£150
1836	*	£6	£50	£150
1837	*	£6	£55	£150
VICTORIA				
1838	*	£3	£30	£110
1839	*	£3	£25	£85

COPPER FARTHINGS

	F	VF	EF	BU
1840	*	£3	£35	£75
1841	*	£3	£35	£90
1842	*	£35	£100	£225
1843	*	£3	£40	£100
1843 I for 1	£40	£200	£500	*
1844	£35	£100	£600	£2000
1845	*	£4	£30	£120
1846	*	£6	£60	£140
1847	*	£3	£40	£125
1848	*	£4	£40	£110
1849	*	£20	£225	£600
1850	*	£3	£35	£100
1851	*	£15	£50	£150
1851 D over D	£10	£75	£300	£850
1852	*	£12	£50	£140
1853 w.w. raised ...	*	£2	£30	£100
1853 ww inc	*	£5	£70	£100
1854 ww inc	*	£3	£30	£75
1855 ww inc	*	£3	£40	£120
1855 ww raised ...	*	£6	£40	£100
1856	*	£4	£50	£135
1856 R over E	£10	£50	£250	£850
1857	*	£3	£30	£100
1858	*	£3	£30	£100
1859	*	£15	£50	£150
1860 proof	*	*	*	£5500

Bronze farthings

VICTORIA

	F	VF	EF	BU
1860 RB	*	£2	£15	£75
1860 TB/RB (mule)	£50	£175	£400	*
1860 TB	*	£1	£15	£75
1861	*	£1	£12	£75
1862 small 8	*	£2	£12	£65
1862 large 8	£50	£150	£600	*
1863	£20	£40	£150	£300
1864	*	£3	£20	£80
1865	*	£3	£20	£80
1865–5/2	*	£5	£25	£110
1865–5/3	*	£3	£15	£30
1865 small 8	*	£2	£18	£35
1865–5/3	*	£1	£10	£30
1866	*	£2	£18	£70
1867	*	*	£20	£80
1868	*	£1	£20	£100
1869	*	£8	£40	£100
1872	*	£2	£18	£70
1873	*	£3	£20	£70
1874 H	*	£3	£25	£65
1874 H G's over G's			Extremely rare	
1875 5 berries/large date	*	£10	£25	£100
1875 5 berries/small date	£8	£20	£90	£300
1875 4 berries/small date	*	£35	£125	£400
1875 H	*	£2	£10	£65
1876 H	*	£10	£45	£200
1877 proof				£5000
1878	*	£2	£10	£70
1879	*	*	£10	£70
1879 large 9	*	£1	£12	£70
1880 4 berries	*	£2	£15	£70
1880 3 berries	*	£2	£15	£70
1881 4 berries	*	£5	£20	£70
1881 3 berries	*	£5	£20	£70

	F	VF	EF	BU
1881 H 3 berries ...	*	£2	£12	£60
1882 H	*	£1	£12	£60
1883	*	£3	£28	£95
1884	*	*	£10	£38
1886	*	*	£10	£38
1887	*	*	£18	£40
1890	*	*	£10	£38
1891	*	*	£10	£38
1892	*	£7	£28	£85
1893	*	*	£8	£30
1894	*	*	£12	£40
1895	*	£12	£50	£250
1895 OH	*	*	£3	£12
			£5	£30

Victoria 1896, Old Head Farthing

	F	VF	EF	BU
1897 bright finish ...	*	*	£3	£30
1897 black finish higher horizon ...	*	*	£2	£30
1898	*	*	£3	£30
1899	*	*	£2	£30
1900	*	*	£2	£30
1901	*	*	£2	£15

Edward VII, 1907 Farthing

EDWARD VII

1902	*	*	£3	£20
1903 low horizon ...	*	*	£4	£20
1904	*	*	£4	£20
1905	*	*	£4	£20
1906	*	*	£4	£20
1907	*	*	£4	£20
1908	*	*	£4	£20
1909	*	*	£4	£20
1910	*	*	£5	£25

GEORGE V

1911	*	*	*	£15
1912	*	*	*	£15
1913	*	*	*	£15
1914	*	*	*	£15
1915	*	*	*	£15
1916	*	*	*	£15
1917	*	*	*	£15
1918 black finish ...	*	*	*	£10
1919 bright finish ...	*	*	*	£9
1919	*	*	*	£9
1920	*	*	*	£10
1921	*	*	*	£10
1922	*	*	*	£10
1923	*	*	*	£10
1924	*	*	*	£10
1925	*	*	*	£10

	F	VF	EF	BU
926 modified effigy	*	*	*	£6
927	*	*	*	£6
928	*	*	*	£3
929	*	*	*	£3
930	*	*	*	£3
931	*	*	*	£3
932	*	*	*	£3
933	*	*	*	£3
934	*	*	*	£5
935	*	*	£1.50	£7
936	*	*	*	£2

George VI 1951 farthing (wren on reverse)

GEORGE VI
	F	VF	EF	BU
1937	*	*	*	£2
1938	*	*	*	£4
1939	*	*	*	£3
1940	*	*	*	£3
1941	*	*	*	£3
1942	*	*	*	£3
1943	*	*	*	£3
1944	*	*	*	£3
1945	*	*	*	£3
1946	*	*	*	£3
1947	*	*	*	£3
1948	*	*	*	£3
1949	*	*	*	£3
1950	*	*	*	£3
1951	*	*	*	£3
1952	*	*	*	£3

ELIZABETH II
	F	VF	EF	BU
1953	*	*	*	£2
1954	*	*	*	£2
1955	*	*	*	£2
1956	*	*	*	£4

Fractions of farthings

COPPER HALF FARTHINGS

GEORGE IV
	F	VF	EF	BU
1828 Britannia breaks legend	£5	£20	£75	£200
1828 Britannia below legend	£8	£35	£125	*
1830 lge date	£5	£25	£85	£225
1830 sm date	£6	£30	£100	*

WILLIAM IV
	F	VF	EF	BU
1837	£15	£75	£250	*

Victoria 1839 half farthing

BRONZE FARTHINGS
	F	VF	EF	BU
VICTORIA				
1839	*	£2	£25	£85
1842	*	£2	£25	£85
1843	*	*	£10	£40
1844	*	*	£10	£35
1844 E over N... ...	£3	£12	£75	£250
1847	*	£3	£20	£55
1851	*	£3	£25	£60
1852	*	£3	£25	£60
1853	*	£4	£40	£95
1853 proof				£350
1854	*	£4	£60	£125
1856	*	£5	£50	£110
1856 large date ...	£6	£25	*	*
1868 bronze proof	*			£300
1868 copper-nickel proof	*			£400

COPPER THIRD FARTHINGS
	F	VF	EF	BU
GEORGE IV				
1827	*	£10	£40	£100
WILLIAM IV				
1835	*	£10	£50	£125
VICTORIA				
1844	*	£15	£50	£150
1844 RE for REG ...	£20	£50	£200	*
1844 large G in REG	*	£15	£50	£150

BRONZE THIRD FARTHINGS
	F	VF	EF	BU
VICTORIA				
1866	*	*	£15	£40
1868	*	*	£15	£40
1876	*	*	£15	£45
1878	*	*	£15	£40
1881	*	*	£15	£40
1884	*	*	£10	£30
1885	*	*	£10	£30

Edward VII 1902 third farthing

EDWARD VIII
	F	VF	EF	BU
1902	*	*	£8	£25

GEORGE V
	F	VF	EF	BU
1913	*	*	£8	£25

COPPER QUARTER FARTHINGS
	F	VF	EF	BU
VICTORIA				
1839	£3	£10	£30	£75

Victoria 1839 quarter farthing

	F	VF	EF	BU
1851	£4	£12	£40	£85
1852	£3	£10	£30	£75
1853	£5	£12	£40	£85
1853 proof	*	*	*	£550
1868 bronze-proof	*	*	*	£300
1868 copper-nickel proof	*	*	*	£425

Decimal coinage

f denotes face value

ELIZABETH II

BRITANNIAS

A United Kingdom gold bullion coin introduced in the autumn of 1987 contains one ounce of 22ct gold and has a face value of £100. There are also half ounce, quarter ounce and one-tenth ounce versions, with face values of £50, £25 and £10 respectively. All are legal tender.

The Britannia coins bear a portrait of The Queen on the obverse and the figure of Britannia on the reverse.

	B.V.
1987-2005 1oz, proof ...	*
1987-2005 inclusive ½oz, proof	*
1987-2005 inclusive ¼oz, proof	*
1987-2005 inclusive ⅒oz, proof	*

(½ and ¼ oz issued only in sets)

To commemorate the 10th anniversary of the first Britannia issue, new reverse designs were introduced for the gold coins as well as a series of 4 silver coins with denominations from £2 to 20 pence. The silver coins were issued in Proof condition only for 1997.

1997. 1oz, ¼oz and ⅒oz issued individually (all coins issued in 4-coin sets)
1997. 1oz, ¼oz silver coins issued individually (all coins issued in 4-coin sets)
1998. Gold and silver coins issued with new portrait of HM the Queen and first reverse design.
2001. New reverse designs introduced for gold and silver coins.

FIVE POUNDS

1984 gold, BU	£400
1985 – –	£425
1986 – –	£425
1987 – new uncoupled effigy	£425
1988 – –	£425
1989 – BU, 500th anniversary of the sovereign	£450
1990 gold, BU	£435
1990 Queen Mother's 90th birthday, gold, proof	£600
1990 – silver, proof	£100
1990 – cu-ni, BU	£10
1991 gold, BU	£450
1992 gold, BU	£450
1993 40th Anniversary of The Coronation	
gold, proof	£700
1993 – silver, proof	£32
1993 – cu-ni, BU	£10
1993 gold BU	£475
1994 gold BU	£500
1995 gold BU	£535
1996 Queen's 70th birthday, gold, proof ...	£645
1996 – silver, proof	£33
1996 – cu-ni, BU	£10
1996 – gold, BU	£575
1997 Golden Wedding, gold, proof	£650
1997 – silver, proof	£32
1997 – cu-ni, BU	£10
1997 – gold, BU	£535
1998 Prince Charles 50th Birthday, gold, proof	£600
1998 – silver, proof	£50
1998 – cu-ni, BU	£10
1998 – gold, BU	£500
1999 Diana Memorial, gold, proof	£600

(Gold versions also listed in FIVE POUNDS section of milled gold.) In 1984 the Royal Mint issued the first of an annual issue of Brilliant Uncirculated £5 coins. These bear the letter 'U' in a circle.

1999 – silver, proof	£45
1999 – cu-ni, BU	£10
1999 Millennium, gold, proof	£600
1999 – silver, proof	£33
1999 cu-ni, BU	£10
1999 gold, BU	£500
2000 Millennium, gold, proof	£495
2000 silver with 22 carat gold, proof	£37
2000 cu-ni, BU	£10
2000 Queen Mother commemorative, gold, proof	£495
2000 silver, proof	£35
2000 silver, piedfort	£68
2000 cu-ni, BU	£10
2000 gold, BU	£500
2001 Victorian Era anniversary	
gold, proof	£525
gold proof with reverse frosting	£750
silver, proof	£35
silver, proof with reverse frosting ...	£70
cu-ni, BU	£10
gold, BU...	£400
2002 Golden Jubilee, gold, proof...	£600
2002 – Silver, proof	£35
2002 cu-ni BU...	£10
2002 Sheild reverse, gold, proof	£600
2002 Queen Mother memorial, gold, proof	£600
2002 –, Silver, proof	£35
2002 cu-ni BU...	£10
2003 BU	£535
2003 proof	£650
2004. Entende Cordiale, gold, proof...	£600
2004.-, platinum, piedfort, proof	£3000
2004.-, ,silver, piedfort, proof..	£150
2004. -, ,silver, proof....	£35
2004.-, ,cu-ni, proof...	£14
2004.-, ,specimen, ...	£10
2004.-, ,B.U...	£5
2005.Trafalgar, gold, proof...	£600
2005.-, ,silver, piedfort, proof..	£150
2005. -, silver, proof...	£35
2005.-, ,cu-ni, proof...	£15
2005.-, ,specimen, ...	£10
2005 BU Trafalgar	£5
2005.Nelson, gold, proof...	£600
2005.-, ,silver, piedfort, proof..	£150
2005. -, silver, proof...	£35
2005.-, ,cu-ni, proof...	£15
2005.-, ,BU., ...	£5
2005 BU Nelson	£10
2006.Queen's 80th Birthday, gold, proof.	£745
2006.-, ,silver, proof..	£40
2006. -, B.U....	£5

TWO POUNDS

1983 gold, proof...	£225
1986 Commonwealth Games (nickel brass)	£4
1986 –, in folder, BU	£6
1986 silver unc	£15
1986 – – proof	£35
1986 gold, proof...	£225
1987 gold, proof...	£250
1988 gold, proof...	£250
1989 Bill of Rights (nickel brass)	£4
1989 –, in folder, BU	£6
1989 – silver, proof	£30
1989 Claim of Right (nickel brass)	£4
1989 Bill of Rights (nickel brass)	£4
1989 –, in folder, BU	£6

(For 1989 £2 piedforts see sets)

1989 500th anniversary of the sovereign,	
gold, proof...	£275
1990 gold, proof...	£250
1991 gold, proof...	£250
1993 gold, proof	£250

1994 Bank of England, gold, proof	£425
1994 –, gold 'mule', proof	£800
1994 –, silver, proof	£30
1994 –, silver piedfort, proof	£60
1994 –, in folder, BU	£8
1994	£4
1995 50th Anniverary of end of Second World War, silver, proof	£27
1995 ditto, in folder, BU	£8
1995 –, silver, piedfort, proof	£60
1995 –, gold, proof	£375
1995 50th Anniversary of United Nations, gold, proof	£300
1995 –, in folder, BU	£6
1995 –, silver, piedfort, proof	£60
1995 –, proof	£30
1995	£4
1996 European Football, gold, proof	£350
1996 –, silver, proof	£27
1996 –, silver, piedfort...	£65
1996 –, in folder, BU	£6
1996	£4
1997 Bimetal, gold, proof	£350
1997 –, silver, proof	£29
1997 –, in folder, BU	£6
1997 silver, piedfort	£60
1997	£4
1998 Bimetal, silver, proof	£29
1998 – silver, piedfort	£50
1998 – proof	£6
1998 –, in folder, BU	£6
1998	£4
1999 Rugby World Cup, gold, proof...	£300
1999 – silver, proof	£30
1999 – silver, piedfort	£150
1999 –, in folder, BU	£6
1999	£4
2001 Marconi commemorative, gold, proof	£295
2001 – silver, proof	£29
2001 – silver, proof with reverse frosting ...	£29
2001 – silver, piedfort	£50
2001 – in folder, BU	£6
Four different reverse designs were issued in sets	
2002 Commonwealth Games, gold,proof ...	*
2002 Commonwealth Games, silver,proof	*
2002 Commonwealth Games, piedfort	*
2002 Commonwealth Games, BU	*
2002 Shield reverse, gold,proof	£300
2003 DNA Gold ti-metal proof	£295
2003 Britannia, silver, proof...	£35
2003 Britannia, silver	£14
2003 Silver proof DNA	£30
2003 DNA in folder	£7
2004. Locomotive, gold, proof...	£350
2004.-, ,silver, piedfort, proof..	£50
2004. -, silver, proof...	£30
2004.-, ,BU, silver...	£15
2004-, ,specimen...	£10
2005. 400th Gunpowder Plot gold, proof..	£350
2005.-, ,silver, piedfort, proof..	£50
2005. -, silver, proof...	£30
2005.-, ,specimen, ...	£7
2005 Gold proof WWII	£325
2005 Silver proof piedfort WWII	£49
2005 WWII, silver proof	£30
2005 in folder BU WWII	£9
2005 Britannia, silver proofl	£40
2005 -, silver l	£14
2006 Brunel the Man, gold, proof	£385
2006 -, silver, proof...	£30
2006 -, presentation	£20

ONE POUND

1983	£2

1983 Unc, in folder	£5
1983 silver, proof	£35
1983 – – piedfort...	£125
1984 Scottish reverse	£2
1984 – Unc, in folder	£5
1984 – silver, proof	£20
1984 – – piedfort...	£55
1985 New portrait, Welsh reverse	£4
1985 – – Unc, in folder	£5
1985 – – silver, proof	£22
1985 – – piedfort...	£55
1986 Northern Ireland reverse	£5
1986 – Unc, in folder	£5
1986 – silver, proof	£25
1986 – – – piedfort	£60
1987 English reverse	£4
1987 – Unc, in folder	£4
1987 – silver, proof	£30
1987 – – piedfort	£55
1988 Royal Arms reverse	£5
1988 – Unc, in folder	£5
1988 – silver, proof	£35
1988 – – – piedfort	£55
1989 Scottish rev as 1984, silver, proof ...	£20
1989 – – – silver, piedfort...	£50
1990 Welsh reverse as 1985	£5
1990 – silver, proof	£30
1991 Northern Ireland rev as 1986, silver proof	£25
1992 English rev as 1987, silver, proof	£25
1993 Royal Coat of Arms (reverse as 1983), silver, proof	£30
1993 – – – piedfort	£65
1994 Scottish Lion, silver, proof	£35
Ditto, Unc. in folder	£5
1994 – silver, piedfort	£55
1995 Welsh dragon, silver, proof	£25
Ditto, Unc in folder, Welsh version	£5
1995 – silver, piedfort	£55
1996 Northern Ireland Celtic Ring	
Unc in folder	£5
Silver, proof	£27
Silver, piedfort	£55
1997 English Lions Unc, in folder	£5
silver, proof	£30
silver, piedfort	£55
1998 Royal coat of arms/reverse as 1983, silver, proof	£25
silver, piedfort	£45
1999 Scottish Lion (reverse as 1984) new portrait, silver proof	£25
silver proof, reverse testing...	£40
silver, piedfort	£45
2000 Welsh Dragon (reverse as 1995) new portrait, silver, proof	£25
silver proof, reverse testing	£40
silver, piedfort	£47
2001 Northern Ireland (reverse as 1996) new portrait, silver, proof	£25
silver, piedfort	£45
-in folder, BU	£4
2002 English design (reverse as 1997) silver, proof	£27
silver, piedfort	£49
in folder, BU	£5
2003 Silver proof	27
2003 – (Royal Arms,) piedfort, silver, proof	£45
2004 Forth Rail Bridge, gold, proof	£325
2004 – piedford, silver, proof	£45
2004 – silver, proof	£25
2004 – specimen...	£5
2005 Gold proof Menai Bridge	£345
2005 Silver proof piedfort Menai Bridge ...	£49

2005 in folder BU	£5
2006 Bridge sewes, gold, proof	£365
2006 – silver, proof	£29
2006 – presentation	£5

2001.Note that the edge inscriptions on £2 and £1 appear either upright or inverted in relation to the obverse.

FIFTY PENCE

1969	£1
1970	£1
1973 EEC	£1
1973 – proof	£3
1976-1981	f
1982 rev changed to FIFTY PENCE	f
1983, 1985	f
1992 European Community	£5
1992 – silver, proof	£30
1992 – silver, proof piedfort	£55
1992 – gold, proof	£400
1994 Normandy landing	£2
1994 – silver, proof	£28
1994 – silver, piedfort	£50
1994 – gold, proof	£400
1997 new size (27.3mm diameter) silver, proof	£27
silver, piedfort	£46
1997 old and new size,silver proofs	£50
1998, 1998	f
1998 European Presidency	£2
1998 – silver, proof	£25
1998 – silver, piedfort	£45
1998 – gold, proof	£250
1998 National Health Service Commemorative	£2
1998 – silver, proof	£25
1998 – silver, piedfort	£45
1998 – gold, proof	£250
1999 Britannia reverse	*
2000 Library Commemorative	£2
2000 –, in folder, BU	£5
2000 –, silver, proof	£25
2000 –, silver, piedfort	£47
2000 –, gold, proof	£250
2003 –, Suffragette, presentation	£5
2004 –, Roger Bannister, gold proof	£265
2004 –, Roger Bannister, silver proof pied fort	£46
2004 Roger Bannister, silver proof	£25
2004 –, proof	£5
2004 –, presentationt	£5
2005 –, gold, proof Samuel Johnson	£265
2005 –, silver, proof Samuel Johnson	£26
2005 –, silver proof piedfort Samuel Johnson	£49
2005 Samuel Johnson, proof	£5
2005 Victoria Cross, proof gold	£325
2006 Victoria Cross, The Heroic Acts,	

proof, gold	£365
2006 – Victoria Cross, silver, proof	£27
2006 Victoria Cross, The Heroic Acts,	
proof, silver	£27

TWENTY-FIVE PENCE

1972 Silver Wedding	£1
1972 – silver, proof	£30
1977 Jubilee	£1
1977 – silver, proof	£20
1980 Queen Mother's 80th birthday	£1
1980 – in blister pack	£3
1980 – silver, proof	£50
1981 Royal Wedding	£1
1981 – in folder	£3
1981 – silver, proof	£30
Coronation, Anniv. Silver proof...	£35
Coronation, Anniv. folder	£10
Coronation, Anniv	£5
Coronation, Anniv. Gold proof crown	£555

TWENTY PENCE

1982	f
1982 silver, proof piedfort	£50
1983-5, 1987-2003	f

TEN PENCE

1968	£0.25
1969	£0.25
1970	£0.20
1971	£0.20
1973	£0.20
1974-1977, 1979-1981	f
1992 new size (24.5mm diameter)	
silver, proof, piedfort...	£40
1992 old and new size, silver, proofs	£30
1992, 1995, 1997-2003 – cu-ni	f

FIVE PENCE

1968-1971	*
1975, 1977-1980, 1987, 1988, 1989	f
1990 silver, proof, old and new	£26
1990 silver, piedfort	£30
1990, 1991, 1992, 1994-1999-2003 – cu-ni ...	f

TWO PENCE

1971	*
1973-1981	*
1985 new portrait, rev changed to	*
1986-2003	f

ONE PENNY

1971	*
1973-1981	*
1982 rev changed to ONE PENNY	f
1983, 1984	f
1985 new portrait	f
1986-2003	f

HALF PENNY

1971	*
1973-81	*
1982 instead of 1/2 NEW PENNY	*
1983	*

Proof and Specimen Sets

Proof or specimen sets have been issued since 1887 by the Royal Mint in official cases. Prior to that date, sets were issued privately by the engraver. Some sets are of currency coins, easily distinguishable from proofs which have a vastly superior finish. The two 1887 sets frequently come on to the market, hence their place in this list. The 1953 'plastic' set, though made up of currency coins, is official. It was issued in a plastic packet, hence the name. Apart from the seats stated, as being uncirculated, currency or specimen, all those in the following listing are proof sets.

GEORGE IV FDC
New issue, **1826**. Five pounds to farthing (11 coins) £22500

WILLIAM IV
Coronation, **1831**. Two pounds to farthing (14 coins) £20000

VICTORIA
Young head, **1839**. 'Una and the Lion' five pounds plus sovereign to farthing (15 coins) £35000
Young head, **1853**. Sovereign to half farthing, including 'Gothic' crown (16 coins) £27000
Jubilee head, Golden Jubilee, **1887**. Five pounds to Threepence ('full set' – 11 coins) £7000
As above, currency set (unofficial) £1700
Jubilee head, Golden Jubilee, **1887**. Crown to threepence ('short set' – 7 coins) £1200
As above, currency set (unofficial) £250
Old head, **1893**. Five pounds to threepence ('full set') – 10 coins) £8000
Old head, **1893**. Crown to threepence ('short set' – 6 coins) £1500

EDWARD VII
Coronation, **1902**. Five pounds to Maundy penny – matt proofs (13 coins) £1650
Coronation, **1902**. Sovereign to Maundy penny – matt proofs (11 coins) £625

GEORGE V
Coronation, **1911**. Five pounds to Maundy penny (12 coins) £3250
Coronation, **1911**. Sovereign to Maundy penny (10 coins) £950
Coronation, **1911**. Halfcrown to Maundy penny (8 coins) £450
New types, **1927**. Crown to threepence (6 coins) £350

GEORGE VI
Coronation, **1937**. Gold set, five pounds to half sovereign (4 coins) £2500
Coronation, **1937**. Silver and bronze set, crown to farthing including Maundy money (15 coins) ... £275
Mid-century, **1950**. Halfcrown to farthing (9 coins) £100
Festival of Britain, **1951**. Crown to farthing (10 coins) £125

ELIZABETH II
Coronation, **1953**. Crown to farthing (10 coins) £95
Coronation, **1953**. Currency ('plastic') set, official, halfcrown to farthing (9 coins) £15
Specimen decimal set, **1968**. 10p, 5p; **1971** 2p, 1p, ½p in wallet (5 coins) £1
Last £sd coins, **1970**. (sets issued 1971-73). Halfcrown to Halfpenny (8 coins) £18
Proof decimal set, **1971**. (issued 1973), 50p, 10p, 5p, 2p, 1p, ½p (6 coins) £15
Proof decimal set, **1972**. 50p, Sliver Wedding, 25p, 10p, 5p, 2p, 1p, ½p (7 coins) £20
Proof decimal sets, **1973, 1974, 1975, 1976**. 50p, to ½p (6 coins) ... ... · £12
Proof decimal set, **1977**. 50p to ½p, plus Jubilee crown (7 coins) £12
Proof decimal set, **1978**. 50p to ½p (6 coins) £12
Proof decimal set, **1979**. 50p to ½p (6 coins) £12
Proof decimal set, **1980**. 50p to ½p (6 coins) £10
Proof gold set, **1980**. Five pounds, two pounds, sovereign, half sovereign (4 coins) £800
Commemorative proof coin set, **1981**. Five pounds, sovereign, Royal Wedding Silver crown,
  50p to ½p (9 coins) £550
Commemorative set, **1981**. Sovereign and Royal Wedding silver crown (2 coins) £125
Proof decimal set, **1981**. 50p to ½p (6 coins) £10
Proof gold set, **1982**. Five pounds, two pounds, sovereign, half sovereign (4 coins) £800
Proof decimal set, **1982**. 50p to ½p including 20p (7 coins) £12
Uncirculated decimal set, **1982**. 50p to ½p including 20p (7 coins) ... ... · £9
Proof gold set, **1983**. Two pounds, sovereign, half sovereign (3 coins) £325
Proof decimal set, **1983**. £1 to ½p (8 coins) £18
Uncirculated decimal set, **1983**. £1 to ½p (8 coins) £14
Proof gold set, **1984**. Five pounds, sovereign, half sovereign (3 coins) £575
Proof decimal set, **1984**. £1 (Scottish rev) to ½p (8 coins) £16
Uncirculated decimal set, **1984**. £1 (Scottish rev) to ½p (8 coins) £13
Proof gold set, **1985**. new portrait. Five pounds, two pounds, sovereign, half sovereign (4 coins) £750
Proof decimal set, **1985**. new portrait. £1 (Welsh rev) to 1p (7 coins) in de luxe case £20
Proof decimal set, **1985**. As above, in standard case £16
Uncirculated decimal set, **1985**. £1 (Welsh rev) to 1p (7 coins) £12
Proof gold set, **1986**. Commonwealth Games two pounds, sovereign, half sovereign (3 coins) £350
Proof decimal set, **1986**. Commonwealth Games £2, Northern Ireland £1.50p to 1p (8 coins),
  de luxe case £25
Proof decimal set, **1986**. As above in standard case £20
Uncirculated decimal set, **1986**. As above, in folder £12
Proof gold Britannia set, **1987**. One ounce, half ounce, quarter ounce tenth ounce (4 coins) £650
Proof decimal set, **1987**. Quarter ounce, tenth ounce (2 coins) £150

Proof gold set, **1987**. Two pounds, sovereign, half sovereign (3 coins) **£325**
Proof decimal set, **1987**. £1 (English rev) to 1p (7 coins) in de luxe case **£23**
Proof decimal set, **1987**. As above, in standing case **£18**
Uncirculated decimal set, **1987**. As above, in folder **£10**
Proof gold Britannia set, **1988**. One ounce, half ounce, quarter ounce, tenth ounce (4 coins) **£650**
Proof gold Britannia set, **1988**. Quarter ounce, tenth ounce (2 coins) **£150**
Proof gold set, **1988**. Two pounds, sovereign, half sovereign (3 coins) **£325**
Proof decimal set **1988**. £1 (Royal Arms rev) to 1p (7 coins) in de luxe case **£26**
Proof decimal set, **1988**. As above, in standard case **£19**
Uncirculated decimal set, **1988**. As above, in folder **£11**
Proof gold Britannia set, **1989**. One ounce, half ounce, quarter ounce, tenth ounce (4 coins) **£700**
Proof gold Britannia set, **1989**. Quarter ounce, tenth ounce (2 coins) **£150**
Proof gold set, **1989**. 500th anniversary of the sovereign. Five pounds, two pounds, sovereign,
  half sovereign (4 coins) **£1500**
Proof gold set, **1989**. 500th anniversary of the sovereign. Two pounds, sovereign, half sovereign (3 coins) ... ...
  ... ... **£750**
Proof decimal set, **1989**. Bill of Rights £2. Claim of Right £2,
  £1 (Scottish rev as 1984), 50p to 1p (9 coins) in de luxe case **£35**
Proof decimal set, **1989**. As above, in standard case **£30**
Proof silver, Bill of Rights £2. Claim of Right £2. **1989**. (2 coins) **£60**
Proof silver piedfort, **1989**. £2 as above (2 coins) **£80**
Uncirculated. **1989**. As above (2 coins) in folder **£15**
Uncirculated decimal set, **1989**. £1 (Scottish rev as 1984) to 1p (7 coins) **£22**
Proof gold Britannia set, **1990**. **£850**
Proof gold set, **1990**. Five pounds, two pounds, sovereign, half-sovereign (4 coins) **£850**
Proof gold set, **1990**. Two pounds, sovereign, half sovereign (3 coins) **£450**
Proof silver set, **1990**. Five pence (23.59mm diam) and five pence (18mm diam, new size) **£30**
Proof decimal set, **1990**. £1 (Welsh rev as 1985) to 1p including large and small 5p (8 coins) in deluxe case ... **£30**
Proof decimal set, **1990**. As above, in standard case **£25**
Uncirculated decimal set, **1990**. £1 (Welsh rev as 1985) to 1p including large and small 5p (8 coins) **£20**
Proof gold Britannia set, **1991**. **£850**
Proof gold set, **1991**. Five pounds, two pounds, sovereign, half-sovereign (4 coins) **£850**
Proof gold set, **1991**. Two pounds, sovereign, half sovereign (3 coins) **£450**
Proof decimal set, **1991**. £1 to 1p (7 coins) in deluxe case **£30**
Proof decimal set, **1991**. As above, in standard case **£25**
Uncirculated decimal set, **1991**. (7 coins) **£20**
Proof gold Britannia set, **1992**. **£850**
Proof gold set, **1992**. Five pounds, two pounds, sovereign, half sovereign (4 coins) **£850**
Proof gold set, **1992**. Two pounds, sovereign, half sovereign (3 coins) **£450**
Proof silver set, **1992**. Ten pence (large and small size) **£30**
Proof decimal set, **1992**. £1 (English rev as 1987) to 1p (two 50p, new 10p) (9 coins) in deluxe case **£32**
Proof decimal set, **1992**. As above, in standard case **£28**
Uncirculated decimal set, **1992**. **£20**
Proof gold Britannia set, **1993**. **£850**
Proof gold set, **1993**. Five pounds, two pounds, sovereign, half sovereign (4 coins) **£1000**
Proof gold set, **1993**. Two pounds, sovereign, half sovereign (3 coins) **£450**
Proof decimal set, **1993**. Coronation Anniversary £5, £1 to 1p (8 coins) in deluxe case **£35**
Proof decimal set, **1993**. As above, in standard case **£30**
Uncirculated decimal set, **1993** (with two 50p, no £5) (8 coins) **£25**
Proof gold Britannia set, **1994**. **£850**
Proof gold set, **1994**. Five pounds, two pounds Bank of England, sovereign, half sovereign (4 coins) **£950**
Proof gold set, **1994**. Two pounds Bank of England, sovereign, half sovereign (3 coins) **£500**
Proof decimal set, **1994**. £2 Bank of England, £1 (Scottish rev), 50p D-Day to 1p (8 coins) in deluxe case **£35**
Proof decimal set, **1994**. As above, in standard case **£30**
Uncirculated decimal set, **1994**. **£14**
Proof gold Britannia set, **1995**. **£850**
Proof godl set, **1995**. Five pounds, two pounds Peace, sovereign, half sovereign (4 coins) **£800**
Proof gold set, **1995**. Two pounds Peace, sovereign, half sovereign (3 coins) **£450**
Proof decimal set, **1995**. Two pounds Peace, £1 (Welsh rev) to 1p (8 coins) in deluxe case **£36**
Proof decimal set, **1995**. As above, in standard case **£29**
Uncirculated decimal set, **1995**. **£12**
Proof gold Britannia set, **1996**. **£900**
Proof gold set, **1996**. Five pounds, two pounds, sovereign, half sovereign (4 coins) **£800**
Proof gold set, **1996**. Two pounds, sovereign, half sovereign (3 coins) **£400**
Proof silver decimal set, **1996**. £1 to 1p (7 coins) **£100**
Proof decimal set, **1996**. 60th Birthday £5, £2 Football, £1 Northern Irish rev to 1p (9 coins) in deluxe case **£38**
Proof decimal set, **1996**. As above, in standard case **£32**
Proof gold Britannia set, **1997**. **£1000**
Uncirculated decimal sert, **1996**. £2 to 1p (8 coins) **£11**
Proof gold set, **1997**. Five pounds, two pounds (bimetal), sovereign, half sovereign (4 coins) **£800**
Proof gold set, **1997**. Two pounds (bimetal), sovereign, half sovereign **£450**
Proof silver set, **1997**.Proof silver Britannia set, **1997**. Two pounds to 20p **£85**
Proof decimal set, **1997**. Fifty pence (large and small size) **£65**
Golden Wedding £5, £2 bimetal. £1 (English rev) to 1p, with new 50p in deluxe case **£40**
Proof decimal set, **1997**. As above, in standard case **£35**
Uncirculated decimal set, **1997**. As above but no £5 (9 coins) **£11**
Proof gold Britannia set, **1998**. **£1000**

Proof gold set, **1998,** £5 to half sovereign	**£900**
Proof gold set, **1998,** £2 to half sovereign	**£450**
Proof silver set, Britannia **1998,** £2 to 20p	**£100**
Proof decimal set, **1998,** Prince Charles, £5 to 1p in deluxe case	**£40**
Proof decimal set, **1998,** as above, in standard case	**£33**
Uncirculated set, **1998,** as above but no £5 (9 coins)	**£15**
Proof silver set, **1998,** 'EU' and 'NHS' 60p (2 coins)	**£50**
Proof gold Britannia set, **1999.**	**£1000**
Proof gold set, **1999,** £5, £2 Rugby World Cup, sovereign, half sovereign	**£900**
Proof gold set, **1999,** £2 Rugby World Cup, sovereign, half sovereign	**£450**
Proof decimal set, **1999,** Diana £5 to 1p in deluxe case	**£40**
Proof decimal set, **1999,** as above, in standard case	**£35**
Uncirculated set, **1999,** as above but no £5 (8 coins)	**£15**
Proof gold, Britannia set, **2000**	**£900**
Proof gold, **2000,** £5 to half sovereign	**£1000**
Proof gold, **2000,** £2 to half sovereign	**£500**
Proof silver decimal set, **2000,** £5 to 1p plus Maundy coins (13 coins)	**£245**
Proof decimal set, **2000,** Executive (10 coins)	**£70**
Proof decimal set, **2000,** Deluxe (10 coins)	**£40**
Proof decimal set, **2000,** Standard (10 coins)	**£30**
Proof gold Britannia set, **2001,** new reverse designs	**£890**
Proof gold set, **2001,** Five pounds, £2 Marconi commemorative, sovereign, half sovereign	**£900**
Proof gold set, **2001,** £2 Marconi commemorative, sovereign, half sovereign	**£415**
Proof silver Britannia set, **2001,** new reverse designs, Two pounds to 20p	**£90**
Proof decimal set, **2001,** Executive (10)	**£75**
Proof decimal set, **2001,** Deluxe (10)	**£48**
Proof decimal set, **2001,** Gift (10)	**£43**
Proof decimal set, **2001,** Standard (10)	**£34**
Uncirculated set, **2001,** as above but no £5 (9)	**£14**
Proof gold set, **2002,** £5 to half sovereign, new reverse design	**£1000**
Proof gold set, **2002,** £2 to half sovereign, new reverse design	**£425**
Proof gold set, **2002,** Golden Jubilee £5, £2 bimetal, £1 (English rev) to 1p plus maundy coins (13 coins) ...	**£3000**
Proof gold set, **2002,** Commonwealth Games £2 (England, N. Ireland, Scotland and Wales)	**£1150**
Proof silver set, **2002,** Commonwealth Games £2 (England, N. Ireland, Scotland and Wales)	**£98**
Proof gold Britannia set, **2002**	**£875**
Proof silver piedfort set, **2002,** Commonwealth Games £2 (England, N. Ireland, Scotland and Wales)	**£195**
Proof decimal, **2002,** Executive (9) Golden Jubilee £5, £2 bimetal, £1 (English rev) to 1p	**£70**
Proof decimal, **2002,** Deluxe (9)	**£46**
Proof decimal, **2002,** Gift (9)	**£40**
Proof decimal, **2002,** Standard (9)	**£32**
Uncirculated set, **2002,** As above but no £5 (8)	**£14**
Uncirculated set, **2002,** Commonwealth Games £2 (England, N. Ireland, Scotland and Wales)	**£15**
Proof gold set, **2003,** £5 to half sovereign	**£1000**
Proof gold set, **2003,** £2 to half sovereign (DNA £2)	**£425**
Proof decimal set, **2003,** Executive (11)	**£69**
Proof decimal set, **2003,** Deluxe (11)	**£47**
Proof decimal set, **2003,** Standard (11)	**£34**
Uncirculated set, **2003,** (10)	**£14**
Proof Gold set, **2004** £2 to half sovereign (3)	**£425**
Proof Gold set, **2004,** Entente Cordiale (2)	**£965**
Proof Gold set, **2004,** D-Day Anniversary, Crowns (3)	**£187**
Proof Gold Britannia set, **2004** (4)	**£900**
Proof Gold Britannia set, **2004** (3)	**£415**
Proof Silver set, **2004,** Entente Cordial (2)	**£69**
Proof Silver set, **2004,** D-Day Anniversary, crowns (3)	**£250**
Uncirculated set, **2004,** 'New coin pack', (10)	**£9**
Proof Decimal, **2004,** Deluxe (10)	**£40**
Proof Decimal, **2004,** Executive (10)	**£65**
Proof Decimal, **2004,** Standard (10)	**£29**
Proof gold Britannia set, (4)	**£800**
Proof gold set, **2005,** £5 to half-sovereign (4)	**£995**
Proof gold set, **2005,** £2 to half-sovereign (3)	**£450**
Proof decimal set, **2005,** Executive (12)	**£75**
Proof decimal set, **2005,** Deluxe (12)	**£49**
Proof decimal set, **2005,** Standard (12)	**£38**
Uncirculated set, **2005,** (10)	**£14**
Gold Proof Britannia set, **2005,** (4)	**£935**
Gold Proof Britannia set, **2005,** (3)	**£429**
Silver Predfort set (4)	**£189**
Proof Gold Set, **2006,** (3)	**£580**
Proof Gold Set, **2006,** Brunel £2 (2)	**£770**
Proof Gold Set, **2006,** Victoria Cross 50p (3)	**£650**
Proof Silver Set, **2006,** 80th Birthday (13)	**£275**
Proof Silver Set, **2006,** Britannia (5)	**£275**
Proof Silver Set, **2006,** Brunel £2 (2)	**£60**
Proof Executive Act, **2006,** (13)	**£78**
Proof Deluxe Act, **2006,** (13)	**£50**
Proof Standard Act, **2006,** (13)	**£40**

Scottish Coins

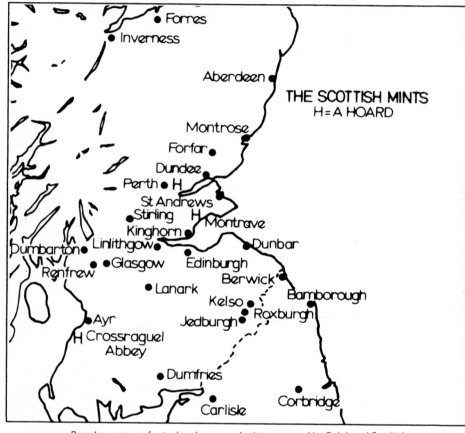

THE SCOTTISH MINTS
H = A HOARD

Forres
Inverness
Aberdeen
Montrose
Forfar
Dundee
Perth H
St Andrews
Stirling H
Montrave
Kinghorn
Dumbarton
Linlithgow
Dunbar
Renfrew
Glasgow
Edinburgh
Berwick
Lanark
Kelso
Bamborough
Ayr
Jedburgh
Roxburgh
Crossraguel Abbey
Dumfries
Carlisle
Corbridge

Based on a map of actual and supposed mints prepared by Spink and Son Ltd.

The number of mints which have been in operation in Scotland can be seen from the map above. The mints of the first coinage of Alexander III are the greatest number ever working together in Scotland, and it is this area that really attracts the collector of the different mint issues. For this reason, when we deal with this reign later on, we give a price for issues of each mint town, but not for any other reign.

MINT TOWN	KING(S)
ABERDEEN	Alexander III, David II Robert III, James I, II, III
AYR	Alexander III
BAMBOROUGH	Henry
BERWICK	David I, Malcom IV, William I, Alexander II, III Robert Bruce, James III
CARLISLE	David I, Henry
CORBRIDGE	Henry
DUMBARTON	Robert III
DUMFRIES	Alexander III
DUNBAR	William I ?, Alexander III
DUNDEE	William I ?, Alexander III
DUNFERMLINE	William I
FORFAR	Alexander III
FORRES	Alexander III
GLASGOW	Alexander III
INVERNESS	Alexander III
JEDBURGH	Malcom IV
KELSO	Alexander II
KINGHORN	Alexander III
LANARK	Alexander III
LINLITHGOW	James I, II
MONTROSE	Alexander III
PERTH	William I, Alexander III, Robert II to James II
RENFREW	Alexander III
ROXBURGH	Alexander III
ST ANDREWS	Alexander III
STIRLING	Alexander III, James I, II Mary Stuart

Prices are for the commonest coins in each case. Collectors should expect to pay these amounts and upwards. For further details see The Scottish Coinage, by I. Stewart (Spink, 1967, reprint 1975) and Coins of Scotland, Ireland and The Islands, Spink 2003. Gold coins are indicated. All other coins are silver unless another metal is stated.

	F	VF
DAVID I 1124-53	F	VF
Pennies	£525	£1250

Four different groups; struck at the mints of Berwick, Carlisle, Roxburgh and
| Edinburgh | £750 | £1850 |

This superb David I penny of Carlisle realised £1,210 in Spink's Douglas auction in 1997

HENRY 1136-52
(Earl of Huntingdon and Northumberland)
| Pennies ... ... | £1750 | £5000 |

Three types; struck at the mints of Corbridge, Carlisle and Barnborough.

MALCOLM IV 1153-65
| Pennies ... ... | £5000 | £12500 |

Five types; struck at the mints of Roxburgh and Berwick.

WILLIAM THE LION 1165-1214
| Pennies ... ... | £85 | £225 |

Three issues; struck at the mints of Roxburgh, Berwick, Edinburgh, Dun (Dunfermline?), Perth

ALEXANDER II 1214-49
| Pennies ... ... | £750 | £2250 |

Mints of Berwick and Roxburgh, varieties of bust.

Halfpenny and farthing of Alexander III and penny of Robert Bruce

ALEXANDER III 1249-86
1st coinage pennies 1250-80
Mints

	F	VF
Aberdeen	£110	£275
Ayr	£175	£500
Berwick	£70	£150
'DUN'	£135	£375
Edinburgh	£80	£175
Forfar	£200	£650
Fres	£200	£600
Glasgow	£150	£375
Inverness	£175	£475
Kinghorn	£250	£750
Lanark	£185	£525
Montrose	£675	£1500
Perth	£75	£185

SCOTTISH COINS

	F	VF
Renfrew	£450	£1000
Roxburgh	£70	£160
St. Andrews	£150	£450
Stirling	£135	£375
'TERWILANER' (uncertain name)	£250	*

2nd coinage c. 1280 –
Many types and varieties
Pennies	£30	£75
Halfpennies	£75	£250
Farthings	£200	£525

JOHN BALIOL 1292-6
1st coinage (rough surface issue)
| Pennies ... ... | £100 | £250 |
| Halfpennies ... ... | £350 | £750 |

2nd coinage (smooth surface issue)
| Pennies ... ... | £135 | £300 |
| Halfpennies ... ... | £150 | £375 |

Robert Bruce Penny

ROBERT BRUCE 1306-29
Pennies	£550	£1250
Halfpennies	£625	£1350
Farthings	ext. rare	

Probably all struck at Berwick.

David II Groat, Edinburgh Mint

DAVID II 1329-71
Nobles (gold)	ext. rare	
Groats	£85	£225
Halfgroats	£75	£200
Pennies	£35	£100
Halfpennies	£325	£900
Farthings	£650	£1250

Three issues, but these denominations were not struck for all issues. Edinburgh and Aberdeen mints.

ROBERT II 1371-90
Groats	£85	£200
Halfgroats	£90	£225
Pennies	£80	£225
Halfpennies	£100	£275

Some varieties. Struck at mints of Dundee, Edinburgh, Perth.

SCOTTISH COINS

ROBERT III 1390-1406 ....

	F	VF
Lion or crowns (gold)	£850	£2250
Demy lions or halfcrowns (gold) ...	£675	£1650
Groats	£75	£175
Halfgroats	£125	£350
Pennies	£225	£575
Halfpennies	£200	£525

Three issues, many varieties. Struck at mints of Edinburgh, Aberdeen, Perth, Dumbarton.

James I Demy or Nine Shilling Piece

JAMES I 1406-37

	F	VF
Demies (gold)	£625	£1350
Half demies (gold)	£750	£2000
Groats	£135	£350
Billon pennies	£150	£400
Billon halfpennies	£375	£850

Mints, Aberdeen, Edinburgh, Inverness, Linlithgow, Perth, Stirling.

JAMES II 1437-60

	F	VF
Demies (gold) from	£625	£1850
Lions (gold) from	£850	£2250
Half lions (gold) from		Very rare
Groats	£175	£500
Halfgroats	£475	*
Billon pennies	£175	£525

Two issues, many varieties. Mints: Aberdeen, Edinburgh, Linlithgow, Perth, Roxburgh, Stirling.

ECCLESIASTICAL ISSUES C 1452-80

	F	VF
Bishop Kennedy copper pennies ...	£75	£200
Copper farthings	£175	£475

Different types, varieties

JAMES III 1460-88

	F	VF
Riders (gold) from	£1350	£3250
Half riders (gold)	£1500	£4000
Quarter riders (gold)	£1750	£4500
Unicorns (gold)	£1500	£3500
Groats ... ...from	£185	£450

James III groat and
James V one-third groat

Halfgroats from	£350	£750
Pennies from	£150	£425
Billon placks from	£100	£275
Billon half placks from	£100	£300

	F	VF
Billon pennies from	£90	£250
Copper farthings from	£275	*

Many varieties. Mints: Edinburgh, Berwick, Aberdeen.

James IV Unicorn

JAMES IV 1488-1513

	F	VF
Unicorns (gold)	£1250	£2750
Half unicorns (gold)	£850	£2000
Lions or crowns (gold)	£1350	£3500
Half lions (gold)	£1750	£5000
Pattern angel (gold)		unique
Groats	£325	£950
Halfgroats	£475	£1250
Pennies (light coinage) ... ...ext rare		*
Billon placks	£40	£100
Billon half placks	£125	£400
Billon pennies	£45	£110

Different types, varieties. Mint: Edinburgh only.

James V 'Bonnet' piece of 1540

JAMES V 1513-42

	F	VF
Unicorns (gold)	£1350	£3250
Half unicorns (gold)	£1750	£4500
Crowns (gold)	£750	£1650
'Bonnet' pieces or ducats (gold) ...	£2500	£6000
Two-thirds ducats (gold)	£2850	£5500
One-third ducats (gold)	£3000	£7500
Groats from	£145	£475
One-third groats	£135	£400

James V groat

Billon placks	£25	£80
Billon bawbees	£25	£75
Billon half bawbees	£75	£200
Billon quarter bawbees		unique

Different issues, varieties. Edinburgh mint.

Note: from here on all Scottish coins were struck at Edinburgh.

MARY 1542-67

1st Period 1542-58

	F	VF
Crown (gold)	£1350	£3500
Twenty shillings (gold)	£2000	£4500
Lions or forty-four shillings (gold)	£1350	£2750

Extremely rare Francis and Mary ducat which realised £77,000 at a Spink auction in March 1997

	F	VF
Half lions or twenty-two shillings (gold)	£1100	£2500
Ryals or £3 pieces (gold) 1555, 1557, 1558	£3500	£7000
Half ryals (gold) 1555,1557,1558 ..	£3750	£8000
Portrait testoons, 1553	£2500	£6500

Mary, Queen of Scots Half Testoon, 1560, Francis and Mary

	F	VF
Non-portrait testoons, 1555-8	£200	£575
– half testoons, 1555-8	£250	£650
Billon bawbees	£35	£100
– half bawbees	£65	£150
– pennies (facing bust)	£200	£575
– pennies (no bust) 1556	£125	£475
– lions, 1555, 1558	£30	£90
– placks, 1557	£45	£125

2nd period (Francis and Mary) 1558-60

	F	VF
Ducats or sixty shillings (gold) ...	ext. rare	
Non-portrait testoons, 1558-61 ...	£200	£575
– half testoons, 1558-60	£225	£675
Twelvepenny groats (Nonsunt) 1558-9	£65	£150
– lions, 1559-60	£30	£80

3rd period (widowhood) 1560-5

	F	VF
Crown (gold) 1562	ext. rare	
Portrait testoons, 1561-2	£1750	£4500
– half testoons, 1561-2	£2000	£6000

4th period (Henry and Mary) 1565-7

	F	VF
Portrait ryals, 1565	ext. rare	
Non-portrait ryals, 1565-7	£300	£700

Mary and Henry 1565 two thirds ryal

	F	VF
– two thirds ryals, 1565-7	£275	£675
– – undated	£800	£2000
– one-third ryals, 1565-6	£325	£850
– testoons, 1565	ext. rare	

5th period (2nd widowhood) 1567

	F	VF
_ Non portrait ryals, 1567	£325	£800
– two thirds ryals, 1567	£300	£725
– one-third ryals, 1566-7	£375	£900

Mints: Edinburgh, Stirling (but only for some bawbees)

JAMES VI

Before English accession 1567-1603

1st coinage 1567-71

	F	VF
Ryals 1567-71	£300	£750
Two-third ryals –	£250	£650
One-third ryals –	£300	£700

Superb gold £20 piece of 1575 realised £30,800 in Spink auction in March 1997

2nd coinage 1571-80

	F	VF
Twenty pounds (gold)	£17,500	£40,000
Nobles, 1572-7, 1580	£75	£250
Half nobles –	£70	£225
Two merks, 1578-80 –	£1350	£3000
Merks, 1579-80	£2500	*

3rd coinage 1580-81

	F	VF
Ducats (gold), 1580	£3250	£7500
Sixteen shillings, 1581	£2000	£4500
Eight shillings, 1581	£1350	£3000
Four shillings, 1581	£2500	*
Two shillings, 1581	ext. rare	

SCOTTISH COINS

	F	VF
4th coinage 1582-88		
Lion nobles (gold)	£3500	£8000
Two-third lion nobles (gold)	£3750	£8500
One-third lion nobles (gold)	£4000	£9000
Forty shillings, 1582	£4250	£12000
Thirty shillings, 1582-6	£375	£1050
Twenty shillings, 1582-5	£275	£900
Ten shillings, 1582-4	£250	£850

James VI twenty shillings, 1582

	F	VF
5th coinage 1588		
Thistle nobles (gold)	£1500	£3250
6th coinage 1591-93		
Hat pieces (gold) 1591-3	£3000	£7000
Balance half merks, 1591-3	£175	£525
Balance quarter merks, 1591	£375	£1050
7th coinage 1594-1601		
Riders (gold)	£725	£1650
Half riders (gold)	£625	£1350
Ten shillings, 1593-5, 1598-1601 ...	£110	£275
Five shillings, 1593-5, 1598-1601 ...	£100	£225
Thirty pennies, 1595-6, 1598-9, 1601	£100	£300
Twelve pennies, 1594-6	£85	£225

James VI Sword and Sceptre piece, 1601

	F	VF
8th coinage 1601-4		
Sword and sceptre pieces (gold) ...	£400	£950
Half sword and sceptre pieces (gold)	£350	£850
Thistle-merks, 1601-4	£65	£175
Half thistle merks –	£65	£175
Quarter thistle-merks –	£45	£150
Eighth thistle-merks, 1601-3	£35	£110
Billon and copper issues		
Billon placks or eight penny groats	£20	£65
Billon half packs	£135	£375
Billon hardheads	£25	£85
Billon saltire placks	£135	£425

	F	VF
Copper twopence 1597	£75	£225
Copper penny 1597	£450	*
After English accession 1603-25		
Units (gold)	£575	£1350
Double crowns (gold)	£750	£2000
Britain crowns (gold)	£425	£900
Halfcrowns (gold)	£450	£1000
Thistle crowns (gold)	£375	£900
Sixty shillings	£350	£900
Thirty shillings	£125	£275
Twelve shillings	£125	£325
Six shillings	£375	£900
Two shillings	£35	£110
One shilling	£60	£150

James VI Gold Unit
(after English accession)

	F	VF
Sixpences	*	*
Copper twopences	£20	£50
Copper pennies	£135	£375

Charles I Briot Unit, 3rd coinage

	F	VF
CHARLES 1652-49		
1st coinage 1625-36		
Units (gold)	£875	£2500
Double crowns (gold)	£1250	£3250
Britain crowns (gold)	ext. rare	
Sixty shillings	£575	£2250
Thirty shillings	£150	£400
Twelve shillings	£150	£475
Six shillings	£325	£850
Two shillings	£60	£185
One shillings	£75	£225
2nd coinage 1636		
Half merks	£60	£150
Forty penny pieces	£50	£135
Twenty penny pieces	£65	£165

3rd coinage 1580-81	F	VF
Units (gold)	£825	£1750
Half units (gold)	£950	£2250
Britain crowns (gold)	£975	£2500
Britain half crowns (gold)	£425	£900
Sixty shilling	£325	£1100
Thirty shilling	£135	£350

Charles II, Merk 1669

Charles I Twelve Shillings, 3rd coinage; Falconer's issue.

	F	VF
Twelve shillings	£100	£225
Six shillings	£100	£225
Half Merks	£85	£225
Forty pennies	£35	£90
Twenty pennies	£30	£70
Three shillings	£65	£175
Two shillings	£55	£125
Copper twopences (lion)	£20	£50
– pennies –	£350	*
– twopences (CR crowned)	£15	£35
– twopences (Stirling turners) ...	£15	£35

CHARLES II 1660-85	F	VF
1st coinage		
Four merks		
1664 thistle above bust	£675	£1750
1664 thistle below bust	£675	£1500
1665	£950	*
1670	£850	*
1673	£750	£1750
1674 F below bust	£625	£1300
1675	£625	£1350

Two merks		
1664 thistle above bust	£475	£1000

	F	VF
1664 thistle below bust	£325	£850
1670	£575	£1250
1673	£300	£750
1673 F below bust	£450	£950
1674	£350	£850
1674 F below bust	£400	£900
1675	£375	£850

Merks		
1664	£95	£275
1665	£110	£325
1666	£275	£625
1668	£225	£550
1669	£65	£225
1670	£65	£225
1671	£65	£225
1672	£75	£235
1673	£75	£325
1674	£135	£400
1674 F below bust	£110	£325
1675 F below bust	£110	£325
1675	£175	£500

Half merks		
1664	£175	£475
1665	£150	£450
1666	£200	£675
1667	£200	£675
1668	£150	£450
1669	£85	£350
1670	£85	£350
1671	£90	£325
1672	£90	£325
1673	£100	£375
1675 F below bust	£100	£325
1675	£125	£375

2nd coinage

Dollars		
1676	£325	£1250
1679	£325	£1250
1680	£375	£1350
1681	£325	£1250
1682	£300	£1000

Half dollars		
1675	£300	£900
1676	£450	£1250
1681	£325	£950

Quarter dollars		
1675	£150	£475
1676	£125	£325
1677	£125	£350
1678	£135	£400
1679	£140	£425
1680	£125	£350
1681	£125	£350
1682	£135	£375

Eighth dollars		
1676	£80	£225
1677	£85	£250
1678/7	£175	£525
1679	£125	£425
1680	£80	£200
1682	£125	£425

Charles II silver two merks 1664

SCOTTISH COINS

Sixteenth dollars

1677	£65	£175
1678/7	£75	£200
1679/7	£100	£350
1680	£75	£200
1681	£65	£175

Charles II 1678 Bawbee

Copper twopence CR" crowned	£20	£60
Copper bawbees, 1677-9	£45	£125
Copper turners, 1677-9	£30	£100

JAMES VII 1685-9

Sixty shillings 1688 proof only[1]	FDC	£2000
– gold proof only[1]		Ext. rare

([1]Struck in 1828, not contemporary)

Forty shillings

1887	£225	£750
1688	£250	£800

James VII 1687 ten shillings

Ten shillings

1687	£135	£425
1688	£175	£600

WILLIAM AND MARY 1689-94

Sixty shillings

1691	£450	£1350
1692	£375	£1100

Forty shillings

1689	£250	£750
1690	£225	£625
1691	£200	£500
1692	£150	£475
1693	£135	£450
1694	£200	£600

Twenty shillings

1693	£375	£1100
1694	£475	£1350

Ten shillings

1689	*	*
1690	£200	£575
1691	£125	£400
1692	£125	£400
1694	£250	£675

William and Mary 1694 five shillings

Five shillings	F	VF
1691	£135	£450
1694	£100	£325
Copper bawbee 1691-4	£50	£135
Copper bodle 1691-4	£30	£100

WILLIAM II 1694-1702	F	VF
Pistole (gold) 1701	£2750	£6750
Half pistole (gold) 1701	£2500	£6500

Sixty shillings

1699	*	*

Forty shillings

1695	£175	£500
1696	£185	£525
1697	£200	£550
1698	£225	£625
1699	£225	£625
1700	£650	£1750

Twenty shillings

1695	£150	£475
1696	£125	£375
1697	£275	£750
1698	£125	£375
1699	£375	£900

Ten shillings

1695	£100	£250
1696	£100	£250
1697	£110	£275
1698	£125	£350
1699	£135	£375

Five shillings

1695	£75	£175
1696	£70	£175
1697	£60	£150
1699	£80	£225
1700	£80	£225
1701	£125	£425
1702	£110	£375
Copper bawbee 1695-7	£75	£325
Copper bodle 1695-7	£45	£150

ANNE 1702-14

Pre-Union 1702-7

Ten shillings

1705	£150	£350
1706	£165	£425

Five shillings

1705	£45	£135
1706	£50	£150

Post-Union 1707-14

see under British milled series

JAMES VIII 1688-1766 (The Old Pretender)

Guinea 1716, gold	FDC	£9000
– silver	FDC	£1250
– bronze	FDC	£1500
Crown 1709		unique
Crown 1716, silver	FDC	£500
– gold		ext. rare
– bronze		ext. rare

NB: All the 1716-dated pieces were struck in 1828
from original dies.

Irish Coins

Hammered Issues 995-1661

Prices are for the commonest coins in each case. It should be remembered that most of the Irish coins of these times are in fairly poor condition and it is difficult to find specimens in VF condition upwards. For more details see The Guide Book to the Coinage of Ireland AD 995 to the present day, by Anthony Dowle and Patrick Finn (ref. DF in the following lists): Spink's Coins of Scotland, Ireland and the Islands, and also Patrick Finn's Irish Coin Values.

All coins are silver unlesss otherwise stated

HIBERNO-NORSEMEN OF DUBLIN 995-1150	F	VF
Pennies, imitative of English coins, many types and varieties ...from	£140	£300

Hiberno-Norse penny, c 1015-1035

Hiberno-Norseman of Dublin Penny c1035-1055

JOHN, as Lord of Ireland c 1185-1199

Halfpennies, with profile portrait	£1650	*
Halfpennies, with facing head	£55	£125
Farthings	£275	£700
Different types,varieties, mints, moneyers.		

JOHN DE COURCY
Lord of Ulster 1177-1205

Halfpenny		unique
Farthings	£650	£1750
Different types,varieties, mints, moneyers.		

John as King of England, Rex/Triangle Penny

JOHN as King of England and Lord of Ireland c 1199-1216	F	VF
Rex/Triangle types		
Pennies ... ...from	£45	£100
Halfpennies	£75	£175
Farthings	£575	£1500
Different types,varieties, mints, moneyers.		

HENRY III 1216-1272

Pennies (c 1251-1254) ... ...from	£35	£90

Dublin only, moneyers DAVI and RICHARD. many varieties.

Edward I Waterford penny

EDWARD I 1272-1307

Pennies ... ...from	£25	£70
Halfpennies	£40	£125

Edward I Farthing, Dublin

Farthings	£75	£200

Dublin,Waterford and Cork. Many different issues.

EDWARD III 1327-1377

Halfpennies Dublin mint		ext. rare

There were no Irish coins struck for Edward II, Richard II, Henry IV or Henry V.

HENRY VI 1422-1461

Pennies, Dublin mint		ext. rare

Edward IV untitled crown groats

EDWARD IV 1461-1483

Untitled crown groats ... ...from	£325	£850
– pennies	£900	£1750
Titled crown groats	£1250	£3500
–halfgroats	£1500	*
– pennies	£1000	*
Cross on rose/-sun groats	£1750	£1500

IRISH COINS

	F	VF
Bust/rose-sun double groats	£1350	£4750
– – groats	£1250	*
– – halfgroats	£1250	*
– – pennies	£1000	*
'English style' groats	£90	£225
– halfgroats	£375	£950
– pennies	£45	£100
– halfpennies	£750	*
Bust/rose groats	£325	£850
– – pennies	£100	£300
copper issues		
Crown/cross farthing	£900	*
– – half farthing	£750	£1750
PATRICIUS/SALVATOR		
Farthing	£675	£1650
3 crowns/sun half-farthing	£850	£2500

This is, of course, a very abbreviated listing of the issues of Edward IV which are numerous and complicated, and still pose numismatics many problems. There are also many varieties and different mints.

RICHARD III 1483-1485

	F	VF
Bust/rose-cross groats	£750	£2750
— halfgroat		unique
— penny		ext.rare
Cross and Pellet Penny	£850	£2000
Three-crown groats	£350	£750
Different mints, varieties, etc.		

HENRY VII 1485-1509
Early issues

	F	VF
Three-crown groats	£75	£200
— halfgroats	£125	£300
— pennies	£350	£950
— halfpennies		ext. rare
Different mints, varieties, etc.		

LAMBERT SIMNEL (pretender) 1487

Three-crown groats	£750	£2250
Different mints, varieties.		

HENRY VII 1485-1509

Henry VII facing bust Groat, Dublin

Later issues

	F	VF
Facing bust groats	£95	£250
— halfgroats	£475	£1350
— pennies	£750	£1750
Crowned H pennies	£850	*

Many varieties. Mainly Dublin. Waterford is extemely rare.

HENRY VIII 1509-1547

	F	VF
'Harp' groats	£50	£140
— halfgroat	£375	£1200

Henry VIII harp groats (with initials HA and HI)

These harp coins carry crowned initials, e.g., HA (Henry and Anne Boleyn), HI (Henry and Jane Seymour), HK (Henry and Katherine Howard), HR (Henricus Rex).

Henry VIII portrait groat

Posthumous issues	F	VF
Portrait groats current for 6 pence	£75	£275
— halfgroats …current for 3 pence	£110	£350
— pennies current for 3 halfpence	£325	£1000
— halfpennies current for 3 farthings	£450	£1250
Different busts, mintmarks etc.		

EDWARD VI 1547-1553

	F	VF
Base shillings 1552 (MDLII)	£575	£1650
— contemporary copy	£50	£200

Mary 1553 shilling

MARY 1553-1558

Shillings 1553 (MDLIII)	£575	£2000
Shillings 1554 (MDLIIII)		ext. rare
Groats		**ext. rare**
Halfgroats		ext. rare
Pennies		ext. rare
Several varieties of the shillings and groats.		

PHILIP AND MARY 1554-1558

Base shillings	£200	£850
— groats	£65	£300
Several minor varieties.		

ELIZABETH I 1558-1603

Base portrait shillings	£250	£950
— groats	£100	£350

Elizabeth I 1561 portrait shilling

	F	VF
Fine silver portrait shillings 1561... ...	£175	£750
— groats –	£225	£850
Base shillings arms-harp	£125	£500
— sixpences –	£85	£300
— threepences –	£110	£425
— pennies –	£30	£100
— halfpennies –	£50	£175

JAMES I 1603-1625

	F	VF
Shillings	£70	£250
— Sixpences	£60	£200

Different issues, busts and mintmarks.

CHARLES I 1625-1649
Siege money of the Irish Rebellion 1642-1649
Siege coins are rather irregular in size and shape.

Kilkenny Money 1642

	F	VF
Copper halfpennies (F)	£275	£950
Copper farthings (F)	£300	*

Inchiquin Money 1642-1646
(The only gold coins struck in Ireland)

	F	VF
Gold double pistoles	ext. rare	
Gold pistoles (F)	ext. rare	
Crowns	£2500	£65600

Inchiquin shilling

	F	VF
Halfcrowns...	£1750	£4500
Shillings	£2250	£6000
Ninepences	£3500	*
Sixpences	£3000	*
Groats (F)	£2500	*
Threepences ... ... ext. rare		*

Three issues and many varieties.

Ormonde Money 1643

	F	VF
Crowns (F)	£425	£850
Halfcrowns (F)	£325	£700
Shillings	£175	£450

Ormonde Money, Halfcrown

Ormonde sixpence

	F	VF
Sixpences (F)	£150	£325
Groats (F)	£125	£275
Threepences	£95	£200
Halfgroats (F)	£450	£950

Many varieties.

Rebel Money 1643

	F	VF
Crowns	£2500	£6500
Halfcrowns	£2750	£7000

Town Pieces 1645-1647
Bandon

	F	VF
Copper farthings (F)	*	*

Kinsale copper farthing

Kinsale

	F	VF
Copper farthings (F)	£425	*

Youghal

	F	VF
Copper farthings (F)	£450	£1750
Brass twopences	ext. rare	
Pewter threepences	ext. rare	

IRISH COINS

	F	VF
Cork		
Shillings **(F)**	£2000	£5250
Sixpences **(F)**	£1000	£2250
Copper halfpennies	£750	*
Copper farthings **(F)**	£450	*
Elizabeth I shillings countermarked		
CORKE **(F)**		ext. rare

Youghal farthing

'Blacksmith's' Money 1649
(Based on English Tower halfcrown)

	F	VF
Halfcrown, varieties	£575	£1350

Dublin Money 1649

Crowns	£3250	£9000
Halfcrowns	£2250	£6000

Charles II Armstrong Issue, Farthing

CHARLES II 1660-1685
Armstrong issues 1660-1661

Copper farthings	£25	£100

Charles II to George IV

This series, of which all the issues except Bank of Ireland tokens were struck in base metal, features a large number of varieties, many of which are unpublished, but there is space here for only the main types and best-known variants. A number of rare proofs have also been omitted.

Except for the 'gunmoney' of James II, Irish copper coins are notably hard to find in the top grades, especially the so-called 'Voce populi' issues and specimens of Wood's coinage (which are reasonably common in the lower grades, apart from the rarities).

We have listed some of the 'gunmoney' of James II in only three grades – Fair, Fine and VF. The majority of these hastily produced coins were not well struck and many pieces with little substantial wear are, arguably, not EF in the strictest sense.

Finally, a note on the dating of gunmoney. In the calendar used up to 1723 the legal or civil year commenced on March 25 in Great Britain and Ireland, so December 1689 came before, not after January, February and March 1689. Coins dated March 1689 and March 1690 were struck in the same month.

CHARLES II	Fair	F	VF	EF
St Patrick's coinage				
Halfpenny	£100	£800	*	*
— star in rev legend	£125	£950	*	*
Farthing	£85	£525	*	*
— stars in rev legend	£100	£600	*	*
— cloud around				
St Patrick	*	*	*	*
— martlet below king	£100	£375	*	*
— annulet below king	£100	£375	£850	*

Charles II St Patrick's Farthing

Regal coinage
Halfpennies

1680 large letters	£10	£40	£135	*
small cross	£8	£35	£125	£450
1680 large letters,	£8	£35	£125	£425
pellets	£8	£35	£125	£425
1681 large letters	*	*	*	*
1681 small letters				
1682 large letters	£10	£50	£150	*
1682 small letters	£8	£35	£125	*
1683	£10	£40	£135	£475
1684	£20	£85	£275	*

JAMES II
Regular coinage
Halfpennies

1685	£10	£45	£150	£575
1686	£10	£40	£135	£525
1687	£35	£275	*	*
1688	£10	£50	£150	*

Emergency coinage
Gunmoney
Crowns

1690	£15	£65	£175	£675
1690 'chubby'				
horseman, sword	£25	£100	£350	*
to E (Sby 6577) ...				
1690 similar (DF 373)	£30	£110	£350	*

James II Gunmoney Crown

	Fair	F	VF	EF
Large halfcrowns				
1689 July	£15	£65	£200	*
1689 August	£10	£40	£175	*
1689 September ...	£10	£40	£175	*
1689 October	£8	£35	£175	*
1689 November ...	£10	£40	£185	*
1689 December ...	£10	£40	£185	*
1689 January	£10	£40	£185	*
1689 February	£8	£35	£135	*
1689 March	£8	£35	£135	*
1690 March	£8	£35	£140	*
1690 April	£8	£35	£140	*
1690 May	£10	£40	£185	*
Small halfcrowns				
1690 April	£25	£100	£325	*
1690 May	£6	£30	£110	£250
1690 June	£8	£35	£120	£300
1690 July	£10	£35	£120	£300
1690 August	£12	£40	£150	£450
1690 September ...	*	*	*	*
1690 October	£35	£150	£450	*
Large shillings				
1689 July	£8	£25	£65	£175
1689 August	£6	£20	£60	£150
1689 September ...	£6	£20	£60	£150
1689 October	£8	£25	£65	£175
1689 November ...	£6	£20	£60	£150
1689 December ...	£6	£20	£60	£135
1689 January	£6	£20	£60	£135
1689 February	£6	£20	£60	£135
1689 March	£7	£20	£60	£150
1690 March	£7	£20	£60	£150
1690 April	£8	£25	£80	£175
Small shillings				
1690 April	£10	£30	£90	£225
1690 May	£7	£20	£60	£150
1690 June	£7	£20	£60	£150
1690 July	*	*	*	*
1690 August	£20	*	*	*
1690 September ...	£20	£125	*	*

James II

Gunmoney, halfcrown, May 1690

	Fair	F	VF	EF
Sixpences				
1689 June	£10	£35	£100	£225
1689 July	£8	£30	£90	£185
1689 August	£8	£30	£90	£185
1689 September ...	£10	£35	£110	£225
1689 October	*	*	*	*
1689 November ...	£8	£30	£90	£185
1689 December ...	£8	£30	£90	£185
1689 January	£10	£35	£100	£225
1689 February	£8	£30	£90	£185
1689 March	*	*	*	*
1690 March	*	*	*	*
1690 April	*	*	*	*
1690 May	£15	£45	£125	*
1690 June	*	*	*	*
1690 October	*	*	*	*
Pewter Money				
Crown	£200	£850	£2750	*
Groat	£135	£575	£1500	£3000
Penny large bust ...	£125	£475	£1200	*
Penny small bust	£100	£400	£1000	*

IRISH COINS

	Fair	F	VF	EF

James II Pewter Money, Halfpenny, 1690

	Fair	F	VF	EF
Halfpenny large bust	£65	£225	£650	*
Halfpenny small bust	£50	£175	£475	*

Limerick Money halfpenny

	Fair	F	VF	EF
Limerick Money				
Halfpenny	£15	£60	£185	£375
Farthing reversed N	£20	£75	£175	£475
— normal N	£25	£85	£225	*

1693 halfpenny

WILLIAM AND MARY

Halfpennies				
1692	£6	£35	£125	*
1693	£6	£35	£125	*
1694	£8	£40	£150	*

WILLIAM III

1696 Halfpenny draped bust	£15	£65	£225	*
1696 Halfpenny crude undraped bust ...	£50	£225	£575	*

GEORGE I
Wood's coinage

1722 harp left	£15	£60	£225	*
1722 harp right ...	£8	£35	£135	£500
1723	£6	£20	£80	£450
1723 obv Rs altered Bs	£7	£25	£100	£475
1723 no stop after date	£7	£25	£85	£450
1723/2	£7	£30	£125	*
1723 star in rev legend	*	*	*	*

IRISH COINS

	Fair	F	VF	EF
1723 no stop before HIBERNIA	£5	£20	£80	£450
1724 head divides rev legend	£7	£30	£125	£575
1724 legend continuous over head	£10	£35	£150	*

George I Wood's farthing, 1723

Farthings

	Fair	F	VF	EF
1722 harp left	£40	£150	£650	*
1723 D: G:	£10	£45	£175	£500
1723 DEI GRATIA ...	£6	£25	£100	£250
1724	£10	£35	£140	£375

GEORGE II
halfpennies

	Fair	F	VF	EF
1736	*	£10	£50	£250
1737	*	£10	£50	£250
1738	£1	£15	£60	£275
1741	*	£10	£50	£250
1742	*	£10	£50	£250
1743	£2	£20	£65	£300
1744	£1	£15	£60	£275
1744/43	£2	£20	£65	£300
1746	£1	£15	£60	£275
1747	*	£10	£50	£225
1748	£2	£15	£75	£300
1749	*	£10	£50	£200
1750	*	£10	£45	£210
1751	*	£10	£45	£210
1752	*	£10	£45	£210
1753	*	£12	£50	£250
1755	*	*	*	*
1760	*	£8	£40	£210

Farthings

	Fair	F	VF	EF
1737	£1	£15	£75	£275
1738	*	£10	£60	£250
1744	*	£10	£50	£225
1760	*	£8	£40	£135

George III, Voce Populi Halfpenny 1760

GEORGE III
Voce populi coinage
Halfpennies (1760)

	Fair	F	VF	EF
Type 1 (DF 565) ...	£40	£175	£500	*

	Fair	F	VF	EF
Type 2(DF 566)	£30	£85	£375	*
Type 3(DF 567)	£35	£150	£450	*
Type 4(DF 569)	£25	£110	£325	*
Type 5(DF 570)	£25	£110	£350	*
Type 6(DF 571)	£25	£110	£350	*
Type 7(DF 572)	£30	£125	£400	*
Type 8(DF 573)	£30	£110	£325	*
Type 9(DF 575)	£40	£150	£450	*
Type 9, P before head (DF 576)	£25	£110	£350	£950
Type 9, P under head (DF 577)	£25	£110	£350	£950

	Fair	F	VF	EF
Farthings (1760)				
Type 1 loop to truncation	£75	£250	£1350	£3500
Type 2 no loop ...	*	*	*	*

London coinage	F	VF	EF	UNC
Halfpennies				
1766	*	£10	£65	£275
1769	*	£10	£70	£275
1769 2nd type	*	£15	£95	£400
1775	*	£10	£75	£350
1776	*	£25	£125	£475
1781	*	£8	£60	£250
1782	*	£8	£55	£200

George III Halfpenny, 1805

Soho coinage

	Fair	F	VF	EF
Penny 1805	£5	£35	£150	£225
Halfpenny 1805 ...	£3	£20	£85	£150
Farthing 1806	£2	£15	£65	£100

Bank of Ireland token coinage

	Fair	F	VF	EF
Six shillings 1804 ...	£85	£225	£550	£600

1804 six shilling Bank of Ireland

	F	VF	EF	UNC
Thirty pence 1808	£25	£100	£325	*
Ten pence 1805 ...	£8	£25	£100	£100
Ten pence 1806 ...	£10	£30	£125	£175
Ten pence 1813 ...	£6	£20	£90	£100
Five pence 1805 ...	£6	£20	£80	£100
Five pence 1806 ...	£8	£25	£90	£120

Bank of Ireland ten pence token, 1813

GEORGE IV

	F	VF	EF	UNC
Penny 1822...	£10	£50	£225	£275
Penny 1823...	£10	£60	£275	£300
Halfpenny 1822 ...	£5	£25	£110	£175
Halfpenny 1823 ...	£5	£25	£125	£200

Free State and Republic

Proofs exist for nearly all dates of the modern Irish coinage. However, only a few dates have become available to collectors or dealers and apart from the 1928 proofs, are all very rare. They have therefore been omitted from the list.

TEN SHILLINGS	F	VF	EF	Unc
1966	*	*	£5	£8
1966	*	*	*	£15

HALFCROWNS	F	VF	EF	Unc
1928	£3	£6	£12	£45
1928 proof	*	*	*	£55

Reverse of halfcrown

	F	VF	EF	Unc
1930	£3	£10	£90	£400
1931	£6	£20	£125	£450
1933	£3	£15	£100	£400
1934	£5	£20	£60	£275
1937	£30	£75	£450	£1500
1939	£3	£6	£15	£65
1940	£3	£5	£10	£50
1941	£4	£6	£20	£60
1942	£4	£6	£20	£55
1943	£70	£150	£850	*
1951	*	£1	£5	£40
1954	*	£1	£5	£40
1955	*	£1	£5	£30
1959	*	£1	£5	£20
1961	*	£1	£5	£25

	F	VF	EF	Unc
1961 mule (normal) obv/pre-1939 rev)	£8	£20	£275	*
1962	*	*	*	£5
1963	*	*	*	£5
1964	*	*	*	£5
1966	*	*	*	£3
1967	*	*	*	£3

1937 florin

FLORINS

	F	VF	EF	Unc
1928	£2	£4	£8	£35
1928 proof	*	*	*	£45
1930	£3	£6	£70	£400
1931	£3	£10	£100	£450
1933	£8	£30	£125	£475
1934	£12	£45	£275	£775
1935	£3	£10	£90	£350
1937	£3	£25	£165	£600
1939	£2	£4	£10	£40
1940	£2	£5	£12	£40
1941	£2	£5	£20	£60
1942	£2	£5	£12	£45
1943	£2750	£5500	£9500	*
1951	*	*	£3	£30
1954	*	*	£3	£25
1955	*	*	£3	£20
1959	*	*	£3	£20
1961	*	£3	£6	£40
1962	*	*	£3	£18
1963	*	*	£3	£18
1964	*	*	*	£5
1965	*	*	*	£5
1966	*	*	*	£5
1968	*	*	*	£5

SHILLINGS

	F	VF	EF	Unc
1928	*	£3	£8	£30
1928 proof	*	*	*	£35
1930	£5	£15	£70	*
1931	£3	£10	£50	£250
1933	£3	£10	£50	£250
1935	£2	£5	£40	£120
1937	£5	£25	£250	£825
1939	*	£3	£6	£35
1940	*	£3	£8	£30
1941	£2	£5	£8	£30
1942	£2	£5	£8	£28
1951	*	£1	£3	£20
1954	*	*	£3	£15
1955	*	*	£3	£18
1959	*	*	£6	£25
1962	*	*	*	£5
1963	*	*	*	£4
1964	*	*	*	£5
1966	*	*	*	£4
1968	*	*	*	£4

SIXPENCES

	F	VF	EF	Unc
1928	*	£1	£3	£20
1928 proof	*	*	*	£25
1934	*	£1	£8	£55
1935	*	£3	£12	£90
1939	*	£1	£5	£35

	F	VF	EF	Unc
1940	*	£1	£5	£25
1942	*	*	£5	£25
1945	£2	£8	£35	£150
1946	£5	£12	£70	£400
1947	£1	£6	£25	£100
1948	*	£2	£8	£30
1949	*	*	£5	£30
1950	£2	£15	£35	£150
1952	*	£1	£4	£18
1953	*	£1	£4	£18
1955	*	£1	£4	£18
1956	*	*	£3	£12
1958	*	£1	£5	£40
1959	*	*	£2	£7
1960	*	*	£2	£7
1961	*	*	£2	£7
1962	*	*	£3	£30
1963	*	*	*	£3
1964	*	*	*	£3
1966	*	*	*	£3
1967	*	*	*	£3

1968 sixpence

	F	VF	EF	Unc
1968	*	*	*	£2
1969	*	*	*	£3

THREEPENCES

	F	VF	EF	Unc
1928	*	£1	£3	£15
1928 proof	*	£1	£3	£20
1933	£2	£5	£45	£200
1934	*	£3	£15	£65
1935	£2	£5	£25	£125
1939	£1	£5	£50	£200
1940	*	*	£10	£30
1942	*	*	£5	£35
1943	*	*	£8	£65
1946	*	*	£5	£30
1948	*	£2	£15	£80
1949	*	*	£5	£30
1950	*	*	£2	£6
1953	*	*	£2	£5
1956	*	*	£1	£4
1961	*	*	*	£3
1962	*	*	*	£3
1963	*	*	*	£3
1964	*	*	*	£3
1965	*	*	*	£3
1966	*	*	*	£3

1967 threepence

	F	VF	EF	Unc
1967	*	*	*	*
1968	*	*	*	*

PENNIES

	F	VF	EF	Unc
1928	*	*	£3	£18
1928 proof	*	*	*	£40
1931	*	£2	£10	£55

	F	VF	EF	Unc
1933	*	£3	£15	£80
1935	*	*	£6	£30
1937	*	*	£9	£50
1938 (unique?)	*	*	*	*
1940	£2	£6	£0?	£400
1941	*	£1	£6	£30
1942	*	*	£3	£15
1943	*	*	£5	£20
1946	*	*	£3	£15
1948	*	*	£3	£15
1949	*	*	£3	£15
1950	*	*	£3	£15
1952	*	*	£2	£7
1962	*	*	£2	£3
1963	*	*	*	£2
1964	*	*	*	£2
1965	*	*	*	£1
1966	*	*	*	£1
1967	*	*	*	£1
1968	*	*	*	£1

HALFPENNIES

	F	VF	EF	Unc
1928	*	£3	£6	£30
1928 proof	*	*	*	£35
1933	£1	£10	£40	£325
1935	*	£5	£25	£200
1937	*	*	£15	£60
1939	£4	£10	£30	£140
1940	*	£10	£35	£165
1941	*	*	£5	£15
1942	*	*	£2	£20
1943	*	*	£3	£15
1946	*	*	£5	£55
1949	*	*	£3	£8
1953	*	*	*	£4
1964	*	*	*	£2
1965	*	*	*	£2
1966	*	*	*	£2
1967	*	*	*	£1.50

FARTHINGS

	F	VF	EF	Unc
1928	*	*	£3	£12
1928 proof	*	*	*	£17
1930	*	*	£5	£18
1931	£1	£3	£8	£30
1932	£1	£3	£10	£35
1933	*	£2	£5	£25
1935	*	£5	£12	£45
1936	*	£6	£15	£50
1937	*	£2	£5	£20
1939	*	*	£3	£12
1940	*	£3	£6	£35
1941	*	£1	£3	£7
1943	*	£1	£3	£7
1944	*	£1	£3	£7
1946	*	£1	£3	£7
1949	*	£2	£5	£10
1953	*	*	£3	£7
1959	*	*	£1	£4
1966	*	*	£2	£6

DECIMAL COINAGE
50p, 10p, 5p, 2p, 1p, ½p
All issues face value only.

SETS

	F	VF	EF	Unc
1928 (in card case)	*	*	FDC	£200
1928 (in leather case)	*	*	FDC	£275
1966 unc. set	*	*	*	£10
1971 specimen set in folder	*	*	*	£5
1971 proof set	*	*	*	£9

The Anglo-Gallic Series

Chronological table of the Kings of England and France in the period 1154-1453

Henry II 1154-89
He was Duke of Normandy and Count of Anjou, Maine and Touraine.
Through his marriage in 1152 with Eleanor of Aquitaine he became Duke
of Aquitaine and Count of Poitou. He relinquished both these titles to his
son Richard who in 1169 did homage to Louis VII of France. In 1185 he forced
Richard to surrender Aquitaine and Poitou to ELEANOR who later – during
Richard's absence – actually governed her provinces.

Louis VII 1137-80

Philip II (Augustus) 1180-1223

Richard I (Coeur de Lion) 1189-99
After his homage to the French King, he was, in 1172, formally installed as
Duke of Aquitaine and Count of Poitou. Although his father forced him in
1185 to surrender Aquitaine and Poitou to his mother he retained actual
government. Later Eleanor ruled in his absence.

John 1199-1216
He lost all provinces of the Angevin Empire except Aquitaine and part of
Poitou.

Henry III 1216-72
In 1252 he ceded Aquitaine to his son Edward.

Louis VIII 1223-26
Louis IX (Saint Louis) 1226-70
Philip III 1270-85

Edward I 1272-1307
He governed Aquitaine since 1252. In 1279 he became Count of Ponthieu
in the right of his wife, Eleanor of Castile. When she died in 1290 the county
went to his son Edward.

Philip IV 1285-1314

Edward II 1307-27
He was Count of Ponthieu as from 1290. In 1325 he relinquished the county
of Ponthieu and the Duchy of Aquitaine to his son Edward.

Louis X 1314-16
Philip V 1316-22
Charles IV 1322-28

Edward III 1327-77
He was Count of Ponthieu and Duke of Aquitaine as from 1325. At the
outbreak of the war in 1337 he lost Ponthieu which was restored to him in
1360. In 1340 he assumed the title of King of France, which he abandoned
again in 1360 as a result of the Treaty of Calais. He then obtained Aquitaine
in full sovereignty and consequently changed his Aquitanian title from
Duke (dux) to Lord (dominus) as the first one implied the overlordship of
the French King. He gave Aquitaine as an apanage to his son, the Prince of
Wales, better known as Edward The Black Prince, b.1330, d.1376, who was
Prince of Aquitaine from 1362 till 1372, although he actually ruled from 1363
till 1371. In 1369, after war broke out again Edward reassumed the French
title, which was henceforth used by the Kings of England until the Treaty
of Amiens in 1802.

Philip VI (de Valois) 1328-50

John II (The Good) 1350-64

Charles V 1364-80

Richard II 1377-99
The son of The Black Prince succeeded his grandfather, Edward III, as King
of England and as Lord of Aquitaine.

Charles VI 1380-1422

Henry IV 1399-1413
He adopted the same titles Richard II had, whom he ousted from the throne.

Henry V 1413-22
From 1417 until 1420 he used the title 'King of the French' on his 'Royal' French
coins. After the Treaty of Troyes in 1420 he styled himself 'heir of France'.

Henry VI 1422-61
He inherited the title 'King of the French' from his grandfather Charles VI.
He lost actual rule in Northern France in 1450 and in Aquitaine in 1453.

Charles VII 1422-61

'All Kings of England in the period 1154-1453 had interests in France. They were Dukes or Lords of Aquitaine, Counts of Poitou or Ponthieu, Lords of Issoudun or they were even or pretended to be, Kings of France itself, and, in those various capacities, struck coins. These coins, together with the French coins of their sons, and of their English vassals, are called Anglo-Gallic coins'.

So starts the introduction of the Bourgey-Spink book by E.R. Duncan Elias on this series. We would also like to thank Messrs Bourgey and Spink for allowing us to use some of the illustrations from the book, as well as the chronological table of the Kings of England and France during the period.

The Anglo-Gallic Coins by E.R.D. Elias is still available from Spink and Son Ltd, London (see Some Useful Books on page 11).

Henry II
Denier,
Aquitaine

HENRY II 1152-68
	F	VF
Denier	£45	£125
Obole	£90	£225

RICHARD THE LIONHEART 1168-99
Aquitaine
	F	VF
Denier	£45	£135
Obole	£40	£140

Poitou
Denier	£40	£90
Obole	£60	£175

Issoudun
Denier	£200	*

ELEANOR 1199-1204
Denier	£50	£125
Obole	£275	*

Edward I
Denier au lion,
during his
father's
lifetime

EDWARD I
During the lifetime of his father 1252-72
Denier au lion	£30	£80
Obole au lion	£45	£120

After succession to the English throne 1272-1307
Denier au lion	£75	£225
Obole au lion	£135	*

Edward I
Obole au lion,
after succession

Denier á la croix longue	£65	£165
Denier au léopard, first type	£30	£70
Obole au léopard, first type	£50	£125
Denier á la couronne	£225	*

The coinage of PONTHIEU (Northern France) under the Edwards
Edward I
	F	VF
Denier	£90	£225
Obole	£70	£200

Edward III
Denier	£135	*
Obole	£225	*

EDWARD II
Gros Turonus Regem	ext. rare	
Maille blanche	ext. rare	
Maille blanche Hibernie	£35	£95

EDWARD III
Gold coins
Ecu d'or	£1200	£2850
Florin	£3000	£7500
Léopard d'or, 1st issue	ext. rare	
Léopard d'or, 2nd issue	£1100	£2750

Edward III Léopard d'or, 2nd issue

Léopard d'or, 3rd issue	£1050	£2500
Léopard d'or, 4th issue	£1350	£3500
Guyennois d'or, 1st type	£2750	£7000
Guyennois d'or, 2nd type	£1500	£3750
Guyennois d'or, 3rd type	£1050	£2500

Silver coins
Gros aquitainique au léopard	£150	£475
Gros tournois à la crois mi-longue	£250	£675
Gros tournois à la croix longue	£100	£275
Sterling	£75	£200
Demi-sterling	£125	£375
Gros au léopard passant	£475	*
Gros à la couronne	£135	£375
Gros au châtel aquitainique	£175	£475
Gros tournois au léopard au-dessus	£70	£200
Gros à la porte	£70	£200
Gros acquitainique au léopard au-dessous	£225	*
Blanc au léopard sous couronne	£60	£135
Gros au léopard sous couronne	£200	£550
Gros à la couronne avec léopard	£150	£425
Sterling à la tête barbue	£300	£800
Petit gros de Bordeaux	ext. rare	
Gros au lion	£125	£325
Demi-gros au lion	£225	*
Guyennois d'argent (sterling)	£100	£225
Gros au buste	£900	*
Demi-gros au buste	£425	£1200

Black coins
Double à la couronne, 1st type	£85	*
Double à la couronne, 2nd type	£75	£225
Double à la couronne, 3rd type	£125	*
Double au léopard	£60	£165
Double au léopard sous couronne	£30	£90
Double guyennois	ext. rare	
Denier au léopard, 2nd type	£25	£80
Obole au léopard, 2nd type	ext. rare	
Denier au léopard, 3rd type	£30	£100
Denier au léopard, 4th type	£30	£90

THE ANGLO-GALLIC SERIES

	F	VF
Obole au léopard, 4th type	£30	£100
Denier au lion	£40	£125

N.B. Some issues of the deniers au léopard of the 2nd and 3rd type are very rare to extremely rare and therefore considerably more valuable.

The coinage of BERGERAC

Henry, Earl of Lancaster 1347-51	£700	£1650
Gros tournois à la croix longue ...	£625	*
Gros tournois à la couronne	£650	£1500
Gros au châtel aquitainque	£450	£1000
Gros tournois au léopard au-dessus	ext. rare	
Gros à la couronne		
Gros à fleur-de-lis		ext. rare
Gros au léopard passant	£950	*
Double	£650	*
Denier au léopard	ext. rare	
Henry, Duke of Lancaster 1351-61		
Gros tournois à la couronne avec léopard	£700	*
Gros au léopard couchant	£700	*
Sterling à la tête barbue	£575	*
Gros au lion	ext. rare	

EDWARD THE BLACK PRINCE 1362-72
Gold Coins

Léopard d'or	£1100	£2750
Guyennois d'or	£1350	£3000
Chaise d'or	£1350	£3000
Pavillon d'or 1st issue	£1000	£2400
Pavillon d'or 2nd issue	ext. rare	
Demi-pavillon d'or		
Hardi d'or		

Edward the Black Prince
Hardi d'or of Bordeaux

Silver Coins

Gros	£675	£1750

Edward the Black Prince Demi-Gros

Demi-gros	£75	£225
Sterling	£60	£135
Hardi d'argent...	£40	£100

Edward the Black Prince Hardi d'argent

Black Coins

Double guyennois	£100	£275
Denier au lion	£45	£125
Denier	£50	£135

RICHARD II 1377-99
Gold Coins

Hardi d'or	£1350	£4000
Demi-hardi d'or	ext. rare	

Silver Coins

Double Hardi d'argent	£675	£1850
Hardi d'argent...	£45	£120

Black Coins

Denier	£75	£225

HENRY IV 1399-1413
Silver Coins

Double Hardi d'argent	£450	£1250

Henry IV Double Hardi d'argent

	F	VF
Hardi d'argent...	£35	£110
Hardi aux genêts...	£150	£500

Black Coins

	F	VF
Denier	£50	£135
Denier aux genêts	£125	£350

HENRY V 1413-22
Gold Coins

	F	VF
Agnel d' or	£3000	£8500
Salut d' or	£4250	£12500

Silver Coins

	F	VF
Florette, 1st issue	£75	£175
Florette, 2nd issue	£125	£300
Florette, 3rd issue	£50	£135
Florette, 4th issue	£60	£150
Guénar	£275	£850
Gros au léopard	£325	*

Black Coins

	F	VF
Mansiois		ext. rare
Niquet	£40	£100
Denier tournois	£65	£150

HENRY VI 1422-53
Gold Coins

	F	VF
Salut d' or	£375	£800
Angelot	£1000	£3000

Henry VI Salut d'or, Paris Mint

Silver Coins

	F	VF
Grand Blanc aux ècus	£50	£125
Petit Blanc	£75	£225
Trésin...		ext. rare

Henry V Grand Blanc, Paris Mint

Black Coins

	F	VF
Denier Parisis, 1st issue	£50	£125
Denier Parisis, 2nd issue	£50	£125
Denier tournois	£60	£135
Maille tournois	£60	£135

N.B. The prices of the saluts and grand blancs are
for the mints of Paris, Rouen and Saint Lô; coins of
other mints are rare to very rare and consequently
more valuable.

Island Coinages

CHANNEL ISLANDS

From the date of their introduction onwards, proofs have been struck for a large number of Channel Islands coins, particularly in the case of Jersey. Except for those included in the modern proof sets these are mostly at least very rare and in the majority of cases have been omitted from the list. A number of die varieties which exist for several dates of the earlier 19th century Guernsey eight doubles have also been excluded. For further information in both cases the reader is referred to The Coins of the British Commonwealth of Nations, Part I, European Territories *by F. Pridmore, published by Spink and Son Ltd.*

GUERNSEY

	F	VF	EF	BU
TEN SHILLINGS				
1966	*	*	*	£2
THREEPENCE				
1956	*	*	*	£2
1959	*	*	*	£2
1966 proof only	*	*	*	£2
EIGHT DOUBLES				
1834	*	£12	£40	£250
1858	*	£12	£40	£250
1864	*	£15	£50	*
1868	*	£10	£40	*
1874	*	£10	£40	*
1885 H	*	*	£12	£60
1889 H	*	*	£10	£50
1893 H	*	*	£10	£50
1902 H	*	*	£10	£25
1903 H	*	*	£10	£25
1910 H	*	*	£12	£30
1911 H	*	£15	£40	£75
1914 H	*	*	£7	£20
1918 H	*	*	£10	£25
1920 H	*	*	£5	£12
1934 H	*	*	£5	£15
1934 H prooflike	*	*	*	£100
1938 H	*	*	*	£5
1945 H	*	*	*	£5
1947 H	*	*	*	£4
1949 H	*	*	*	£4
1956	*	*	*	£1
1959	*	*	*	£1
1966 proof only	*	*	*.	£3
FOUR DOUBLES				
1830	*	*	£30	£175
1858	*	*	£35	£250

Guernsey 1864 four doubles

	F	VF	EF	BU
1864	*	£5	£45	*
1868	*	£5	£45	*

	F	VF	EF	BU
1874	*	*	£45	*
1885 H	*	*	£8	£30
1889 H	*	*	£5	£25
1893 H	*	*	£4	£20
1902 H	*	*	£4	£20
1903 H	*	*	£4	£20
1906 H	*	*	£4	£20
1908 H	*	*	£4	£20
1910 H	*	*	£3	£20
1911 H	*	*	£3	£20
1914 H	*	*	£3	£20
1918 H	*	*	£3	£20
1920 H	*	*	*	£15
1945 H	*	*	*	£5
1949 H	*	*	*	£6
1956	*	*	*	£2
1966 proof only	*	*	*	£2
TWO DOUBLES				
1858	*	£30	£100	£300
1868	*	£30	£100	£275
1874	*	£30	£100	£225
1885 H	*	*	£6	£20
1889 H	*	*	£4	£15
1899 H	*	*	£4	£15
1902 H	*	*	£5	£15
1903 H	*	*	£5	£20
1906 H	*	*	£4	£20
1908 H	*	*	£4	£25
1911 H	*	*	£4	£20
1914 H	*	*	£4	£25
1917 H	*	£10	£30	£100
1918 H	*	*	£2	£10
1920 H	*	*	£3	£10
1929 H	*	*	£2	£6
ONE DOUBLE				
1830	*	*	£20	£60
1868	*	£40	£100	£275
1868/30	*	£40	£100	£275
1885 H	*	*	£4	£10
1889 H	*	*	£2	£5
1893 H	*	*	£2	£5
1899 H	*	*	£2	£5
1902 H	*	*	£2	£5
1903 H	*	*	£2	£5
1911 H	*	*	£2	£8
1911 H new type	*	*	£2	£8
1914 H	*	*	£3	£8
1929 H	*	*	£1	£2
1933 H	*	*	£1	£2
1938 H	*	*	£1	£2

ISLAND COINAGES

SETS

1956 proof	... ...	**£25**
1966 proof	... ...	**£8**
1971 proof	... ...	**£7.25**

For coins post 1971 refer to the Standard Catalogue of World Coins published by Krouse Publications annually. Many commemorative pieces in various metals have been struck and therefore a full list of the complete coinage is beyond the scope of this publication.

JERSEY

CROWN	F	VF	EF	BU
1966	*	*	*	£1
1966 – proof	*	*	*	£3

1/4 OF A SHILLING

	F	VF	EF	BU
1957	*	*	*	£2
1960 proof only	*	*	*	£5
1964	*	*	*	£0.30
1966	*	*	*	£0.75

1/12 OF A SHILLING

	F	VF	EF	BU
1877 H	*	*	£7	£70
1881	*	*	£9	£65
1888	*	*	£8	£60
1894	*	*	£7	£50
1909	*	*	£8	£60
1911	*	*	£5	£30
1913	*	*	£5	£30
1923	*	*	£5	£30
1923 new type	*	*	£7	£30
1926	*	*	£5	£25
1931	*	*	£2	£25
1933	*	*	£3	£15
1935	*	*	£2	£15
1937	*	*	*	£5
'1945' (George VI)[1] ...	*	*	*	£3
'1945' (Elizabeth II)[1] ...	*	*	*	£2
1946	*	*	*	£4
1947	*	*	*	£3
1957	*	*	*	£0.40
1960	*	*	*	£0.20
1964	*	*	*	£0.15
1966	*	*	*	£0.15

The date 1945 on one-twelfth shillings commemorates the year of liberation from German occupation. The coins were struck in 1949, 1950, 1952 and 1954.

1/13 OF A SHILLING

			EF	BU
1841	*	*	£60	£175
1844	*	*	£70	£185
1851	*	*	£75	£195
1858	*	*	£70	£185
1861	*	*	£70	£185
1865 proof only	*	*	*	£650
1866	*	*	£20	£80
1870	*	*	£25	£80
1871	*	*	£25	£80

1/24 OF A SHILLING

			EF	BU
1877 H	*	*	£4	£55
1888	*	*	£4	£40
1894	*	*	£4	£35
1909	*	*	£3	£35
1911	*	*	£3	£30
1913	*	*	£3	£25
1923	*	*	£2	£20
1923 new type	*	*	£2	£20
1926	*	*	£2	£20
1931	*	*	£1	£10
1933	*	*	£1	£10
1935	*	*	£1	£10
1937	*	*	£1	£5
1946	*	*	£1	£5
1947	*	*	£1	£5

1/26 OF A SHILLING

			EF	BU
1841	*	*	£45	£145
1844	*	*	£50	£160
1851	*	*	£45	£135
1858	*	*	£45	£135
1861	*	*	£40	£100
1866	*	*	£20	£95
1870	*	*	£20	£85
1871	*	*	£22	£85

1/48 OF A SHILLING

			EF	BU
1877 H	*	£25	£75	£170

1/52 OF A SHILLING

			EF	BU
1841	*	£40	£150	£350
1841 proof	*	*		£600
1861 proof only	*	*	*	£650

DECIMAL COINAGE

SETS

		BU
1957	... ...	£30
1960	... ...	£15
1964	... ...	£10
1966 (4 coins) proof	... ...	£4
1966 (2 crowns)	... ...	£7
1968/7 1 decimal coins		£2
1972 Silver Wedding (5 gold, 4 silver coins)		£400
1972 - - proof		£450
1972 - - (4 silver coins)		£25

For coins post 1972 refer to the Standard Catalogue of World Coins published by Krouse Publications annually. Many commemorative pieces in various metals have been struck and therefore a full list of the complete coinage is beyond the scope of this publication.

ISLE OF MAN

Contemporary forgeries of several of the earlier Isle of Man coins exist.

COPPER AND BRONZE 1709-1839

Isle of Man, Halfpenny, proof in Silver, 1733

Isle of Man, Penny, 1786

PENNIES	F	VF	EF	Unc
1709	£90	£250	£500	*
1733	£30	£125	£400	*
1733 proof	*	£275	£400	*
1733 silver	*	*	£600	*
1758	£20	£70	£275	*
1758 proof	*	*	*	*
1758 silver	*	*	£1000	*
1786	£10	£40	£200	£400
1786 plain edge proof	*	*	£375	£600
1798	£15	£40	£175	£350
1798 bronzed proof	*	*	£275	£450
1798 AE gilt proof ...	*	*	£700	£1250
1798 silver proof	*	*	£1500	£300
1813	£10	£25	£175	£350
1813 bronzed proof ...	*	*	£225	£400
1839	*	£15	£75	£175
1839 proof	*	*	*	£600

HALFPENNIES	F	VF	EF	Unc
1709	£40	£100	£500	*
1733	£25	£120	£200	£350
1733 proof	*	*	£150	£400
1733 silver	*	*	£325	£500
1758	£20	£50	£150	£375
1758 proof	*	*	*	*
1786	£20	£50	£165	£250
1786 plain edge proof	*	*	£300	£475
1798	£10	£40	£165	£275
1798 proof	*	*	£175	£375
1798 AE gilt proof ...	*	*	*	£750
1813	£8	£30	£110	£225
1813 proof	*	*	£250	£350
1839	*	*	£35	£125
1839 proof	*	*	*	*

FARTHINGS	F	VF	EF	Unc
1839	£10	£25	£45	£125
1839 proof	*	*	*	£400

For coins post 1965 refer to the standard catalogue of world coins published by Krouse Publications annually.

British Paper Money

THE prices listed here are only intended as a guide to values of English bank-notes. Notes with the current Chief Cashier, Andrew Bailey are generally available at a little above face, notes prior to that tend to increase in value, especially the very early notes.

Top condition is the most important factor in banknote pricing although it is quite possible to collect a more attractive selection in lower grades; some notes for example are never seen in better then Very Fine. The prices quoted here, recently updated are for EF and VF, a premium can be expected for first class notes - this is especially relevant to notes of John Bradbury and to a lesser extent, N. F. Warren Fisher.

We have not listed banknotes prior to 1914 as these are all scarce and only available in grades up to Very Fine. The past year has continued to show a healthy demand for material at every level, the emphasis still remaining on quality followed by rarity. The hobby continues to grow at a sensible pace, the shortage of good material being the only drawback.

Reference numbers are according to Vincent Duggleby's *English Paper Money*. 6th edition published by Pam West in October 2002. NEW EDITION OUT SOON.

TREASURY NOTES

Signed by John Bradbury

First Issue

			VF	EF
T8	10s	Red on white. Six digits	£550	£900
T9	10s	Red on white. Prefix 'No'	£375	£600
T10	10s	Red on white. Five digits	£650	£1200
T1	£1	Black on white. Prefix large letters A., B. or C.	£1100	£2200
T2	£1	Black on white. As previous but no full stop after serial letter	£1700	£3250
T3	£1	Black on white. Six digits	£800	£850
T4	£1	Black on white. Large serial number, 'dot' and five digits	£750	£1450
T5	£1	Black on white. Large serial number, 'dash' and five digits	£800	£1450
T6	£1	Black on white. Double prefix letters	£700	from £1350
T7	£1	Black on white. Small type face serial number	£2500	£5500

(Serial number with prefix 'No' are referred to as 'dot' if 'No' is followed by a full stop and 'dash' when a dash is used).

Second issue

			VF	EF
T12	10s	Red on white. Five digits	£300	£430
T13	10s	Red on white. Six digits	£300	£575
T11	£1	Black on white.	£250	£475
T15	10s	Red on white. Arabic overprint	£1500	*
T14	£1	Black on white. Arabic overprint	£3200	*

Third issue

			VF	EF
T16	£1	Green and brown on white	£90	£170
T17	10s	Green and brown on white Black serial no. with 'dot'	£350	£600

COINS MARKET VALUES

			VF	EF
T18	10s	Green and brown on white Black serial no. with 'dash'	£350	£800
T19	10s	Green and brown on white Red serial no. with 'dot'	£900	*
T20	10s	Green and brown on white Red serial no. with 'dash'	£230	£450

Signed by Norman Fenwick Warren Fisher First issue (overall watermark)
T25	10s	Green and brown on white, 'dot'	£150	£320
T26	10s	Green and brown on white, 'dash'	£150	£320
T24	£1	Green and brown on white	£60	£120

Second issue (boxed watermark)
T30	10s	Green and brown on white	£120	£230
T31	£1	Green and brown on white 'dot'	£65	£130
T32	£1	Green and brown on white, sq. 'dot'	£180	£330

Third issue (Northern Ireland)
T33	10s	Green and brown on white	£120	£250
T34	£1	Green and brown on white 'dot'	£70	£160
T35	£1	Green and brown on white, sq. 'dot'	£180	£330

Unissued notes prepared during the Great War (all extremely rare)
T21	5s	Deep violet and green on white (Bradbury)	*
T22	2s 6d	Olive-green and chocolate on white	from £7000
T23	1s	Green and brown on white	from £7500
T27	5s	Violet and green on white (Warren Fisher)	from £5000
T28	2s 6d	Olive-green and chocolate on white	from £5000
T29	1s	Green and brown on white	from £5000

BANK OF ENGLAND NOTES
Cyril Patrick Mahon 1925-29
			EF	UNC
B210	10s	Red-brown	£70	£165
B212	£1	Green	£50	£95
B215	£5	Black on white	£300	£520

Bank of England £1 serial no. 2 sold at auction by Spink and Son Ltd several years ago for £56,000.

John Bradbury
5 shillings.

Basil Gage Catterns 1929-34

			VF	EF
B223	10s	Red-brown	£40	£70
B225	£1	Green (prefix: letter, number, number; e.g.E63)	£25	£55
B226	£1	Green (prefix: number, number, letter)	£65	£150
B228	£5	Black on white	£250	£425

Kenneth Oswald Peppiatt 1934-49

B236	10s	Red-brown (prefix: number, number, letter) 1st period	£65	£100
B251	10s	Mauve 2nd period	£45	£80
B256	10s	Red-brown (prefix: number, number, letter) 3rd period	£120	£200
B262	10s	Red-brown (metal filament) 4th period	£45	£85
B238	£1	Green (prefix: number, number, letter) 1st issue	£40	£60
B248	£1	Pale blue (prefix:A-D) 2nd issue	*	*
B249	£1	Blue (shades) 2nd issue	£14	£25
B258	£1	Green (prefix: number, number, letter) 3rd issue	£40	£75
B260	£1	Green (metal filament) 4th issue	£20	£35
B241	£5	Black on white, one straight edge, three deckled	£225	£300
B255	£5	Black on white, straight edges, metal filament, thick paper	£145	£225
B264	£5	Black on white, straight edges, metal filament, thin paper	£120	£200

Unissued notes of the 1939-45 War (very rare)

B253	5s	Olive-green on pale pink background	from £4000	
B254	2s 6d	Black on pale blue background	from £6000	

Percival Spencer Beale 1949-55

B265	10s	Red-brown (prefix: number, number, letter)	£35	£60
B266	10s	Red-brown prefix: letter, number, number, letter	£20	£50
B268	£1	Green	£6	£12
B270	£5	Black on white	£120	£195

Leslie Kenneth O'Brien 1955-62

			EF	UNC
B271	10s	Red-brown (prefix: letter, number, number, letter)	£15	£30
B272	10s	Red-brown (prefix: number, number, letter)	£80	£180
B286	10s	Red-brown, Queen's portrait	£3	£6
B273	£1	Green	£6	£14
B281	£1	Green (prefix: letter, number, number) Queen's portrait	£3	£6
B282	£1	Green (prefix: number, number, letter). Queen's portrait	£3	£6
B283	£1	Green 'R' variety (letter R found in white space above lower BANK OF ENGLAND panel on reverse	£185	£340
B284	£1	Green (prefix: letter number, number, letter). Queen's portrait	£14	£24
B275	£5	Black on white	£120	£200
B277	£5	Blue, pale green and orange (solid symbols)	£30	£70
B279	£5	Blue, pale green and orange (symbols for £5 white)	£35	£75

Jasper Quintus Hollom 1962-66

B295	10s	Red-brown (prefix: number, number, letter)	£3	£6
B294	10s	Red-brown (prefix: letter, number, number, letter)	£3	£6
B288	£1	Green	£3	£6
B292	£1	Green, 'G' variety ('G' in same position as 'R' as B283)	£5	£10
B297	£5	Blue	£18	£38
B299	£10	Multicoloured	£28	£45

John Standish Fforde 1966-70

B309	10s	Red-brown (prefix: number, number, letter)	£3	£6
B310	10s	Red-brown (prefix: letter, number, number, letter)	£3	£6
B311	10s	Red-brown (prefix: letter, number, number)	£8	£12
B301	£1	Green	£4	£12
B303	£1	Green 'G' variety	£4	£10
B312	£5	Blue (prefix: letter, number, number)	£18	£35
B314	£5	Blue (prefix: number, number, letter)	£18	£35
B316	£10	Multicoloured	£20	£40
B318	£20	Multicoloured	£120	£240

John Brangwyn Page 1970-1980

B322	£1	Green (prefix: letter, letter, number, number)	£3	£5
B324	£5	Blue	£20	£45
B332	£5	Multicoloured (prefix: letter, number, number). 1st series	£14	£34
B334	£5	Multicoloured, L on reverse signifies lithographic printing	£10	£24
B326	£10	Multicoloured	£25	£45

			EF	UNC
B330	£10	Multicoloured A-series	£18	£35
B328	£20	Multicoloured	£40	£75

David Henry Fitzroy Somerset 1980-1988
B341	£1	Green	£2	£4
B346	£10	Multicoloured (prefix: letter, letter, number, number)	£30	£65
B350	£20	Multicoloured	£50	£90
B352	£50	Olive green, brown, grey	£70	£100

George Malcolm Gill (1988-1991)
B353	£5	Blue	£10	£20
B354	£10	Brown	£18	£35
B355	£20	Multicoloured	£40	£75
B356	£50	Multicoloured	£80	£140
B357	£5	Multicoloured (Series E) AO1	£10	£28
B358	£20	Multicoloured	£30	£60

G.E.A. Kentfield (1991-)
B361	£10	Multicoloured	£80	£125
B362	£5	Multicoloured	£8	£20
B366	£10	Multicoloured	£14	£30
B374	£20	Multicoloured	£35	£45
B377	£50	Multicoloured	£65	£95

M.V. Lowther (1999-2004)
B380	£5	Multicoloured	f	£10
B382	£10	Multicoloured	f	£23
B384	£20	Multicoloured	£35	£70
B385	£50	Multicoloured	f	£90
B393	£5	Multicoloured	f	£8
B389	£10	Multicoloured	f	£14
B388	£10	Multicoloured The "Co"	f	£18
B386	£20	Multicoloured And "Co"	f	£30

A.Bailey (2004-)
Bailey signed notes exist in £5, £10 and £20. A £50 is expected.
* Exist but no price can be quoted. f - still face value unless special prefix number, i.e. AO1. Prices on modern notes for EF or/and UNC

A recently dicovered extraordinarily rare Bank of England £100 of 1790 sold at auction by Spink in 2000 for £44,000